# AN EVACUEE

Also by Leslie Scrase:

*Days in the Sun* (children's stories, with Jean Head)
*In Travellings Often*
*Booklet on Anglican/Methodist Conversations*
*Some Sussex and Surrey Scrases*
*Diamond Parents*
*Coping With Death*
*The Sunlight Glances Through* (poetry)
*Some Ancestors of Humanism*

# AN EVACUEE
## Leslie Scrase

UNITED WRITERS
Cornwall

UNITED WRITERS PUBLICATIONS LTD
Ailsa, Castle Gate, Penzance, Cornwall.

British Library in Publication Data:
A catalogue record for this book is
available from the British Library.

ISBN 1 85200 087 2

Printed in Great Britain by
United Writers Publications Ltd
Cornwall.

To the memory of Miss Branch
and Mr and Mrs Sharley
who opened their hearts
as well as their homes.

# Acknowledgements etc.

If any readers recognise themselves and are pleased, they know that my memory has been faithful to them for there are autobiographical elements in this story.

On the other hand, if any readers *think* they recognise themselves and are angry, they should remember that *all* the characters in this book are entirely the figment of my imagination and have no connection with any person living or dead.

I have made use in a few of the stories of a book by W.H. Barrett and R.P. Garrod, published by Routledge in 1976 and called *East Anglian Folklore and Other Tales*.

And in case 'the Skimmington' seems to beggar belief, such things were still happening in the not too distant past. Mine was inspired by one at Appledore in North Devon. Afterwards I read an account of one described by Pam Clatworthy in *The Countryman* magazine. It took place in 1939 and there have been a few others since then.

Between September 1st and 3rd one and a quarter million people, mostly children, were evacuated from our major cities. Many people drifted back and there were further evacuations later in the war. My own school was evacuated twice, the second time when it was discovered that its first haven (Hove) was not very safe. In this story evacuation took place in October 1939. Whether there were any evacuations then, I have no idea, but that was when my sister and I joined our school.

# Contents

# 1

# Summer Holidays

They always went to Bognor for their summer holidays.

Alfie and Eric cycled. It was only about fifty miles. The other five crammed into the Austin 16. But first Mr Wallace had walked endlessly round the garden trying to be patient. Lilian always took so long packing. Mind, she did it well. He had to admit that. Everything neat and orderly, and no one could get more into a trunk.

Gerry kept the two youngsters occupied until just before it was time to go. Then he went round the house checking. He knew what lay ahead. And he was right.

A few miles from home Mrs Wallace started. "Did I shut the windows?"

"Yes mother."

"I wonder if I turned off the gas."

Gerry nudged Roger, "Your turn."

"Yes mother."

"What about the electricity?"

"Yes mother."

"And did I lock the back door?"

"Yes mother."

By now Mr Wallace was miles away in his own world. He puffed his pipe contentedly and drove steadily south towards the coast. He loved to drive. He loved the sea. He loved his family. And he became so immersed in his own contentment that the rest of them might as well not have been there. He hardly even noticed when Gerry started the others on 'I spy'.

"Did you lock the garden gate Dad?" Lilian was worrying again.

"Sorry. What did you say?"

"It's all right mother. We checked it and Dad had done it."

"Good." There was a long pause. "What about the French windows. I didn't do the French windows."

"We did. I did the top bolt and Roger did the bottom."

They began to sing. "Daisy, Daisy, give me your answer do." "Any evening, any day, any time you're Lambeth way . . ." "'I do love to be beside the seaside." And then Mrs Wallace began again.

"I wonder if there's anything else I've forgotten."

"Everything's fine mother. We've checked *everything* very carefully."

And at last she believed them.

"You're good boys," she said as she settled back comfortably and began to enjoy her holiday.

They usually got away soon after 11.00 and arrived at their boarding house in time for lunch. It was always the same boarding house, run by two ladies. They still had their dog. That was all Roger cared about.

Lunch over, they made for the beach. It was family ritual to spend the first afternoon building a huge sand-castle. Eric took charge. He liked to be boss even if he was only the second son. The others humoured him because there was no doubt about it, he was the best sand-castle builder.

It wasn't just sand, that sand-castle. Pebbles and sea-weed were built into it and throughout the afternoon it grew. Roger and Margaret soon lost interest and went off on their own. Not that Roger was on his own. Tony the spaniel had adopted him already. By tea-time the sand-castle was man high and complete. They wouldn't touch it again. Just watch and see how much was left at the end of their holiday. There was usually just a small mound, a shallow moat and a few pebbles.

That year was 1939. On the 3rd of September they were all down on the beach as usual – and Tony was there with Roger. But Mr Wallace had brought a wireless set down to the beach hut and at 11.15 they were all sitting around it waiting for the Prime Minister to speak.

As he announced that the country was at war with Germany

12

again, the adults and the older children listened in silence. Mr and Mrs Wallace looked at their children. There was no doubt in their minds. Alfie and Eric would get their call-up papers before very long. Even Gerry might have to go. They felt sick at heart.

It seemed as though the last war had only just ended. Mr Wallace found his mind going back to the trenches. Images of men hanging dead on the barbed wire, drowned in the mud, blown to bits, flashed before his eyes. Memories of cousins and friends long dead surfaced in his mind. So many had died. Had it all been for nothing? Would his sons come through as he had done – scarred in mind and heart but thankful to be alive?

Alfie went quietly away on his own behind the beach huts and was violently sick. He couldn't tell anyone else but he was scared stiff. He had seen so many films of Hitler screaming at crowds wound up to a fever pitch of rapture; so many films of German military might, of German troops goose-stepping through Austria and Czechoslovakia. And now they were in Poland. How could Britain ever hope to match that kind of power?

Eric's feelings were quite different. He had seen the same films and been excited by them – the troops, disciplined, smart, brave and strong. Now it was his turn.

He would be in uniform soon, part of a smart and powerful force. Patriotism welled up inside him. His generation would show their fathers that they were worthy sons, and as their fathers' generation had fought and won, so his generation would fight and win. Perhaps now his dad would begin to tell him about the old war and all those great battles. It never entered his head to wonder why his father never spoke of such things.

He was going to war. He was going to fight for his country and for Poland and Czechoslovakia and downtrodden people everywhere. He couldn't wait.

Gerry felt different again. He looked at his parents and saw their anguish. He looked at his brothers and recognised the different responses he saw. He was not quite fourteen but he was sensitive enough to see and in part to understand. But what did he feel himself?

He had also seen those films of Hitler's might and he shared Alfie's recognition that it would take some matching. But somehow it all seemed very remote. He wondered if the war would go on long enough for him to have to go. And then he noticed Roger and suddenly the gloom lifted and he laughed.

His laughter brought the others out of their thoughts and his pointing finger raised their heads. Soon they were laughing with him. For at eight years old Roger was glad the country was at war.

It was going to be like cowboys and Indians. He whooped and yelled and galloped across the sand and a very excited dog jumped all round him. He lifted his fingers as six-shooters and fired them enthusiastically at the enemy. "Whoa," he cried as he pulled his horse to a halt. He turned and galloped back down the beach.

None of this touched Margaret at all. She just went on making sand-castles – filling up her bucket with sand and turning it upside down.

The holiday continued – with an element of unreality about it for the older ones that was to last a long time. The war didn't seem to make any difference. Roger and Tony were inseparable and Tony was unforgettable.

> He had a stubby, wagging tail,
> a sad and bloodshot eye,
> and ears that met beneath the chin
> and cheeks for keeping biscuits in.
>
> He called Rog every day at seven
> and took him for a walk.
> He loved to take him in the sea
> and shake himself all over him.
>
> He was the friendliest of dogs.
> He was a perfect pal
> for a boy who liked to be alone
> and longed to call that dog his own.

Holidays over, they went back home. Alfie and Eric returned to their jobs in the city. The others went back to school. Nothing had changed and yet everything was different.

# 2

# The Birth of a Baby

Home was a large house near Croydon. The family had moved there shortly before Roger was born one May morning in 1931.

That morning when Roger was born Lilian went to the bathroom. Still a bit sleepy, it was a moment or two before she realised that it wasn't the toilet she needed. You would have thought she would have known.

After all, this was number four – well five really but she had lost one. And not only that, she had been a midwife before she married. She called her husband.

"George. GEORGE. It's coming and it won't be long. Be quick. Send Alfie for the nurse and bring me a pillow."

She hardly dared move, not to get back to the bedroom anyway. She got a clean sheet from the airing cupboard and some clean cloths. Her husband brought the pillow.

"You'll all have to wash in the kitchen and you must see to breakfast and get the boys off."

"But what about you?"

"Just leave me alone," she snapped impatiently, "and send the nurse up as soon as she comes. Don't stand talking."

He knew better than to argue. He left her to complete her preparations.

"Alfie. Get some clothes on quick and take your bike and call nurse. Be as quick as you can."

"Why don't we use the phone," asked Eric. He was proud of their new phone. Like the car, it was something to boast about at school.

"Because she's not on the phone you idiot," shouted Alfie as he ran for the door.

"No," thought Eric. "That's one snag with phones." None of his pals had phones in their houses so he couldn't talk to them.

Lilian lay down on the bathroom floor. The pains were coming pretty often now. It was lucky she always gave birth so easily. Thirty-seven she was. She ought to have finished with all this, but George so wanted a daughter.

Her mind floated off, as it always did, to that terrible November night in 1917 when she was a midwife across in Essex living with her sister Glad. A man had come to the door to ask her to go to a woman in labour.

"But I'm off duty."

"I've been to the doctor and he's gone to London. His mother told me to come to you."

So of course, she had gone. Her bag was always ready and her acetylene lamp was always kept filled. She had cycled after the man without taking much notice of the route they followed. But it seemed an awfully long way, well outside her district.

"This isn't my district you know. You ought to have got someone local."

"There isn't anyone local," he shouted. "Anyway it's no use moaning now. There's no time."

They came to a low, broken down thatched cottage hidden up a muddy lane.

"This is the place," he said. Then he disappeared and she never saw him again.

She went into the house and found it in complete darkness apart from an oil lamp. Two little children were asleep in the corner lying on straw and covered with an assortment of rags. The woman lay on the bed with newspapers and more rags but no mattress and very little to cover her.

She was well on. Lilian didn't have time to stop and view. She went into the kitchen where there was a little bit of a wood fire. There was a bucket full of water and an old saucepan. She heated up some water, found her soap in her bag and washed her hands.

As she was getting ready she had an uncomfortable feeling that she was being watched. So she asked, "Haven't you got anyone here who can help?"

"No. I had a row with my husband this morning and he's

16

pushed off. His mother went with him. There's no one else."

"So who is going to look after you and the other children?"

"We'll be all right."

"Have you any clothes for the baby?"

"No. I didn't know it was coming yet, did I?"

Lilian got up to see what she could find and bumped her head on a beam. As she looked up she felt sure that she saw a pair of eyes looking at her through a crack in the ceiling. Perhaps the mother in law wasn't so far away after all.

She found an old shirt and tore it up to wrap the baby in. It wasn't long before he came – quite naturally and everything was fine. He gave a good cry and that woke the other children so now there were three pairs of eyes staring at Lilian through the darkness.

She cleaned things up, wrapped the baby, showed him to the other children and then gave him to his mother. Just then the woman's oil lamp sputtered and gave out, leaving a great smell behind.

"Where do you keep your oil?"

"I haven't got any."

Lilian fetched the acetylene lamp from her bike and put that on while she finished cleaning and tidying up as best she could. Then she asked:

"What food is there in the house?"

"I think there's a bit of bread, and there's some milk in a jug."

Lilian went out into the kitchen. She found about half a loaf of stale bread, broke it into the saucepan and poured in most of the milk. There wasn't enough so she added some water and made bread and milk. She gave some to the children as well as to the mother.

"Are you sure you're going to be all right?"

"I expect my mother in law will come back now the baby's here."

Had she seen the watching eyes Lilian wondered?

"What about your husband?"

"No he won't come back."

"Will the man who fetched me help?"

"He's just a man who lives in the village. He won't come."

Lilian made her as comfortable as she could and told her if she had any trouble to call the doctor or the police. Then she set off for home. It was raining and before long her lamp gave out. It was so dark she couldn't see to ride so she got off and pushed her bike.

She got down the muddy lane all right but couldn't seem to get out of the village. She kept going round in circles and must have disturbed someone because he came to his bedroom window. She asked him the way.

"You're miles away," he said, but he gave her directions and she was fine after that.

But she was soaked through. Then the first light of dawn began to make her journey easier and soon it was light enough for her to cycle again. At last she arrived safely home. And there was Glad waiting for her. She had the zinc tub on the hearth and plenty of hot water in the copper boiler, and she had a good fire roaring away in the hearth. Lilian stripped off thankfully and clambered wearily into the water. Later in the day, after a good sleep, she reported to the doctor.

"Well done nurse. She's out of our area but as you delivered the baby you'd better see to things."

And that was that. She wasn't even sure that she could find the place again, but she did. She begged some baby clothes, bedding and a nightdress from some of the better-off patients, and some food and a bit of money. Over the next couple of weeks she did her best to see that the woman and her children were clean and respectable.

Fortunately the woman was as strong as a horse, and they were all pretty healthy. Lilian never actually saw the mother in law, but she was pretty sure that she was there. After a couple of weeks her duty was done and she never saw the family again.

But she always thought of them when she was having her own babies. Not every detail of course. And not now that nurse had come and was talking to her and asking where things were.

And then Roger arrived, born in the bathroom just in time for breakfast. To be truthful Lilian was not all that pleased to see him.

"What, another boy," she sighed. She knew that George would want to go on trying for a girl. Luckily for her, eighteen months later Margaret was born and the family was complete.

# 3

# The Baby Minders

For some unknown reason, Roger had no recollection of the day of his birth. In fact, there was precious little that he could remember from his first few years. But others had their memories: Alfie for one.

Alfie was ten years old when Roger was born. As far as he was concerned, the new baby was nothing but a nuisance.

"Alfie," his mother would call. "Come and give Roger a walk in the pram."

I ask you. A boy pushing a pram. Alfie hated it. And it was even worse when Margaret came along and there were two of them to push.

Alfie always walked up the road to Mollie's house. She was a little bit older than he was, and sweet on him.

"Is Molly in?" he would ask. And if she was, "Would she like to come for a walk?"

Molly's mother wasn't taken in by his blue-eyed innocence but she would call Molly and the two of them would walk further up the road and round to the top gate of the park. Once inside the park Alfie would say casually, "I don't suppose you'd like to push the pram on your own for a bit while I go and see my pals?"

Molly knew what that meant but she didn't mind. Alfie could go and play football if he liked. He knew the price – a kiss – and she enjoyed having the two little children. Roger liked being out with her too. She often took him out of the pram and let him push, or run about with her chasing. She helped him pick dandelions and didn't believe they made you wee. She showed him how to blow a dandelion clock and count the blows.

But Molly wasn't always free. Alfie felt a proper fool pushing the pram into the park, but he wasn't going to miss his game. He parked the pram under a tree and went off to play. That was no problem until the day when Roger first decided to climb out.

He wasn't very sure how to do it. He leaned out further and further until he began to topple. Down he went into the grass with a thump. He half sobbed but there didn't seem much point. There was no one to hear him. So he got up and began to toddle across the grass towards the edge of the park. A ditch ran right round the edge. Molly had always caught him before he could climb down but today Molly wasn't there.

He went straight over the edge of the bank and ran with a bit of a rush right down into the mud and water at the bottom. Splash. It was lovely. He scooped up some of the mud and squeezed it through his hands. He laughed with delight and began to make mud pies and put them on the edge of the water. He wondered what they tasted like. Not nice. He spat and tried to wipe the mud off his lips but his hands were muddy too. And so time passed sitting happily in the mud and enjoying himself.

Someone was shouting. It sounded like Alfie. It sounded like his name but he was enjoying himself. He didn't want Alfie. And Alfie sounded cross. He didn't answer.

Alfie *was* cross. But he was scared too. Where had Roger got to? What had happened to him? Had he been kidnapped? Who would want to kidnap Roger? There was that Sunday School teacher who had offered Dad half a crown for him. Oh God. Where was he?

At last he found him, caked in mud. What would his mum say? He tried to wash off the mud with the ditch water, but it only seemed to make things worse. He picked Roger up and put him in the pram. That was a mistake. Now all the pram things were muddy too. It would be a caning for him and no mistake. But there was nothing for it. He took Roger and Margaret home. Thank goodness she had slept through all this.

The next time Alfie left the pram under the tree, he took Roger out and tied him to the tree. But he was never the most practical of boys. Roger thought it was a great game. It didn't take him long to wriggle free and run back to his ditch.

As the years went by Eric was roped in to take his turn, and

20

then Gerry too. Soon Gerry was the only one who looked after Roger and Margaret. It paid. If they took turns, the older two simply bullied Gerry into doing their turn. But if he volunteered, his dad praised him and rewarded him. So Gerry always volunteered. And he decided that as he had no choice in the matter he would make it as much fun as possible. So both Roger and Margaret enjoyed having him to look after them.

Roger liked the snail races and the races with woodlice but Margaret preferred it when they collected rose petals to make scent with.

Mostly they went out. Gerry cadged the bus fare to take them to see the trains and then made them walk. There was a path which ran high above the railway. Roger liked that and the steam rising up and smothering them all. One day Gerry cadged a bit of extra money and took them down on the platform.

The first train was a steam train hissing and whistling and whooshing. Roger was terrified. He took off. Gerry called him back, but he took no notice. He just ran, up the passageway, out of the station, out to the road and towards his home. He couldn't get far enough away. That awful NOISE.

Gerry grabbed Margaret. "Come back. Roger come back."

Not on your life. Roger wasn't going back there for anyone.

"Roger stop. Please stop. Wait for us. We won't go back down there."

Slowly Gerry's promises got through and Roger was feeling puffed out anyway. He stopped and waited until the others caught him up. They went to the bus stop and rode home. It was always wise to go home on the bus so that Roger and Margaret would talk about the bus. Then Gerry's parents knew that he hadn't simply pocketed the bus fares.

They never went to the railway again. Instead Gerry took them to a new park and 'the new swings'. It was an even longer walk but Gerry told them stories and they didn't seem to notice the distance. Then they enjoyed the swings and slides and round-abouts before going back to the bus stop for the journey home.

One day Margaret wasn't paying attention. The bus came. Roger jumped on and went upstairs. So did Gerry. The bus pulled away and then they saw that Margaret wasn't there. She was still on the bus stop. They hurried down and got off at the next stop and ran all the way back. She didn't seem the least bit worried.

She was just standing waiting for the next bus to come. "Silly, soppy, stupid girl," thought Roger.

When it was wet they had to stay indoors. Margaret collected her dolls. Roger collected his stuffed animals, dogs and teddy bears, and the three of them went into the front room. Roger and Margaret sat down in the huge armchairs and Gerry disappeared behind the sofa with the dolls and animals. Punch and Judy had nothing on the scenes that emerged above the top of that sofa. Gerry could keep them going all morning.

# 4

# School

Roger was four and a half when he went to school. Schooldays all followed pretty much the same pattern. Every day was just the same, First thing in the morning Mr Wallace went into Alfie and Eric.

"Come on you boys. Up you get. We haven't got all day."

Then he went into Gerry and Roger with the same call. If they didn't leap out of bed they got a cold flannel in the face.

They crowded into the bathroom with their dad. He took the wash-basin and they knelt side by side by the bath. There was a big bronze geyser fixed to the corner over the bath. If they were allowed hot water Alfie turned it on.

It exploded into life with a great rush of power and a tremendous rattling and shaking finishing with a sustained roar as it heated the water. But mostly the boys washed in cold and only used the geyser on bath nights. It frightened Roger a bit.

He dilly-dallied over his wash so that he could watch his dad sharpen his cut-throat razor on the leather strop hanging behind the bathroom door.

When they had all finished in the bathroom it was time for Margaret to be called. They all heard their dad.

"How's my little girl today? It's time to get up my darling. The boys have finished. The bathroom is clear."

There was no cold flannel for her. But as the smell of bacon rose from the kitchen the boys dressed hurriedly. No one was served until they were all there. Then came winter's porridge with plenty of sugar and a knob of butter. The bacon, egg and fried bread followed, and toast and marmalade if they wanted it.

"Eat up. There's good children. A good breakfast sets you up for the day," said Lilian as she bustled about them all.

And then it was time for off. Mr Wallace to the office, the three eldest boys by bus to grammar school, and Roger to the church school by the bridge over the railway line.

He enjoyed walking to school with a ball at his feet. He soon met up with pals and they spread all over the road footballing or playing marbles in the gutters. As the girls ran with their hoops Roger and his pals would jeer at them and try to make them lose control. Best of all was when they could hitch a ride on the milkman's float. Years later Roger wrote:

> The milkman's horse began to trot,
> the milk-float ran behind,
> and we who ran and jumped and held
> were taken for a ride.
>
> The milkman turned and growled at us
> who clung on tight behind,
> but we who'd run and jumped and held
> were taken for a ride.
>
> The milkman reached and took his whip
> and flicked it every way
> and we jumped off and ran to school –
> we did it every day.

Well perhaps not *every* day. And the boys were back on their feet before they came to the railway bridge before school.

"Got any money?" Jimmy would ask.

"Only my milk money," Roger would answer.

"Come on then." And he led the way into the sweet-shop.

> That sweetshop by the railway bridge
> before they got to school,
> it tempted them with toffee bars
> and huge bulls-eyes
> and lovely liquorice wood.

24

And every day they went that way
with a ha'penny for school milk —
but the ha'pennies went on toffee bars
and huge bulls-eyes
and lovely liquorice wood.

They ran into the playground stuffing sweets and messing about
until the bell rang.

"Got any fag cards?" asked Jimmy.

"Yeah. Got some new ones Saturday."

"Play yer for them."

So the two of them flicked their cards against the playground
wall to see whose would bounce back furthest. Roger had a good
flick and usually went home with more than he took to school.
And he kept the best of each card for his collection.

When the bell rang they lined up in classes. The infants went
into a classroom on their own. But in his second year Roger found
himself in one of three classes that shared the school hall. After
assembly the children pulled out partitions and divided up the
hall. Often they could hear what was going on in other classes
better than they could hear their own. And then Mr Sherwood
would bellow:

"Wallace. I can't hear myself think. Be silent boy."

"How does he know it's me talking?" Roger wondered. "I'm
not even in his class."

After one of Mr Sherwood's shouts everyone went quiet for a
time. Poor Miss Smythe, Roger's teacher, used to blush. She was
a nice teacher. They all liked her. Come to that they all liked old
Sherwood too. He might shout a bit but he was very fair and
sometimes he was quite a lot of fun. Once when he was taking
them for maths Jimmy and Roger were talking.

"Jimmy Smith. Have you something important to say?"

"Sir. Please sir, I was just telling Roger — er Wallace sir, that
I've got toothache."

"Toothache is it? First tooth or second?"

"One of my first teeth sir."

"Hm. Come and stand by my desk. And you Wallace come
with me." He led Roger outside the classroom and closed the door
behind him. "Now Wallace, you — stand here. Be alert and ready
to return to the class. As soon as I call you, you are to pull the

25

b

door open and run in as fast as you can. Is that understood?"

"Yes sir."

Mr Sherwood returned to the class and to Jimmy. To everyone's surprise he blindfolded Jimmy, swizzled him round and round and round, took something out of his desk and then walked Jimmy all over the place until finally they stopped just by the door.

'Now," he said. "Open wide and show me the tooth that's hurting."

Jimmy opened wide and wiggled one of his teeth. Mr Sherwood took some twine from his pocket and tied one end round the tooth. He tied the other end to the door-knob. Then he took hold of Jimmy and drew him back until the twine was almost taut. The class had watched all this wondering what on earth Mr Sherwood was doing. Holding Jimmy firmly by the arms he said, "Stand right where you are and don't move." Then suddenly he roared, "Wallace."

The door flew open, Jimmy yelled, his tooth flew out, and Mr Sherwood caught Roger just in time to stop him running smack into Jimmy. He untied the twine and gave Jimmy his tooth before sending the boys back to their places.

In addition to Maths and Science and Geography and Woodwork, he took the boys for sport. He always seemed to produce the best football team in the district. Alfie, Eric and Gerry had all played for it before they went on to grammar school, and for most of their school holidays they seemed to do nothing else. As soon as their chores were done they were over to the park to play. Roger was allowed to join in even though he was so small.

His holidays and his brothers' holidays didn't quite coincide. At the beginning of the holidays it didn't matter. But at the end, when he had to go back to school and they didn't, it didn't seem fair. So the first day of school, instead of heading for school he took his bike and rode up into the hills towards 'the new swings'. There was plenty of open country up on the hills.

"This is better than silly old school," he thought as he rode through the woods towards the lakes. The sun shone and he laid his bike on the ground, took off his jacket and stuffed his cap and tie into his jacket pockets. He threw stones into the water for a while. When he tired of that, he went back into the woods and started to build himself a den.

Back at school, the roll was called and he was marked 'absent'. Over coffee Miss Smythe took Mr Sherwood to one side.

"Roger Wallace is absent today. I've never known him be absent without Mrs Wallace letting us know."

"No. She was the same with his brothers. She always let us know. You'd better send the school inspector."

So shortly before lunchtime the school inspector arrived at Roger's home. Mrs Wallace was busy with the washing and she wasn't too worried.

"I'll send the boys to find him," she said, "just as soon as they've had their lunch. And I'll make sure he's at school tomorrow."

The boys were not very pleased to lose their afternoon's football. They grumbled until Mrs Wallace silenced them with, "If there's any more fuss I shall speak to your father."

But when they were on their own with their bikes, Alfie grumbled on.

"It's all very well telling us to find him. How do we know where he's gone."

"You go to Grandma and see if he's there," said Eric, "and I'll go to Auntie Louise."

"He won't be with either of them," said Gerry. "He'll either be on the hills or at the new swings. I think we should all go there. That's where we'll find him."

"It's better if we split up," said Eric. "There's more chance of finding him."

"No," said Alfie. "Gerry's right. If he had gone to Grandma or Auntie they would have let Mum know."

"I still think . . . " Eric began.

"Oh shut up. We'll go over the hills. If we don't find him we can easily split up then."

So the three of them set off for the hills. Roger had grown bored and moved on to the new swings. It was all very well being on holiday when everyone else was at school but he was getting hungry, yet he couldn't go home could he.

"I wonder what time it is," he thought. "I need to get home after school. But I don't know the time. I wonder if that man with his dog can tell me?"

But he couldn't. He didn't have a watch. Roger went back to

the swings. And then he saw three boys on bikes. It was his brothers. His first feeling was one of relief. Then he suddenly realised that he must be in trouble. They had come to take him home. He jumped on his bike and rode off as fast as he could go. But it wasn't long before Alfie and Eric caught up with him, grabbed him and clouted him round the head.

Gerry rode up, "You don't have to do that. Dad will give him all the punishment he needs *and* he'll be in trouble at school."

"You take him home then," said Alfie. "We'll ride on ahead."

They did but only as far as the park and their pals and football. Gerry and Roger rode slowly home.

"It isn't fair," said Roger. "You get holidays but I've got to go to school. Will I be in bad trouble?"

"You'll get a ticking off at school. I don't know what Mum and Dad will say. You'd better tell Mum you're sorry. Say you didn't realise you would be causing such trouble."

So Roger did. His mother gave him some tea and then sent him to bed early. She didn't want George caning him. She didn't like it when George sent them down to the shed to choose a cane, and he didn't realise his own strength. He was built like a blacksmith. She was always having to tell him to go easy. But with Roger in bed he would escape.

Gerry went with him to school the following morning to make sure that he went and to explain.

Miss Smythe didn't make a fuss. She just said, "All your brothers worked hard when they were here and that is why they got to grammar school. They deserve their holidays. If you work hard, you will go to grammar school too and have the same holidays as they do."

So Roger decided to work hard. And anyway, it was quite fun being at school.

Roger didn't know it but his school was a particularly good one. It might not have the fancy uniforms of the private schools but he was well taught. He didn't know *how* he learned to read but he did, very quickly, and Miss Smythe soon persuaded Mrs Wallace to let him join the library. He loved that. He was always getting out new books to read.

And he loved hearing the stories from Homer's Iliad and Odyssey when Miss Smythe told them in class. He enjoyed maths too and the long words that went with it: addition, subtraction,

28

multiplication (that was a smashing word that one) and division. And he liked it when Alfie taught him to spell 'difficulty' – Mrs D, Mrs I, Mrs F F I, Mrs C, Mrs U, Mrs L T Y.

He enjoyed *everything*. He was that sort of a boy. Everything except perhaps scripture. But there was one scripture lesson he would never forget.

# 5

# The Scripture Lesson

The vicar had not had a very good morning.

First of all there had been a letter from the bishop. It was a very gentle letter, very polite. But there was no hiding the fact that he was critical of the innovations the vicar had begun to make at the parish church. The bishop had received letters of complaint from life-long parishioners who were not happy.

And it was all so trivial. It had begun when he decided to put a cross on the altar. And it had gone on from there.

And now he had to take those wretched children for Scripture. He didn't feel cut out for talking to children. He didn't even like children. And there had been that silly little incident on the pavement. It was not going to be his day. Three classes sat in the main hall with the partitions back.

"Good morning vicar."

"Good morning children. The hymn this morning is 'Jesus loves me, this I know, for the Bible tells me so'."

And then the lesson began. "Now boys and girls. Today I am going to talk about love and respect. I shall begin with respect.

"This morning I met a little girl walking along the pavement. Now tell me, if you meet the vicar on the pavement what should you do?"

There was no answer so the vicar continued, "Rachel Pollard come forward please. Tell the class what you should do if you meet the vicar on the pavement."

Rachel stood at the front of the class, looked at her feet and said nothing.

"You should say, 'Good morning vicar'. Isn't that what you should say Rachel?"

"Yes sir," replied Rachel quietly.

"That's right. That is the polite thing to do. It shows respect, not to me but to God because I am his minister. And then what should you do Rachel?"

There was no answer.

"You should step off the pavement into the road to allow the vicar to pass. That shows both politeness and respect. But the little girl I met this morning neither spoke nor stepped off the pavement did she Rachel?"

"No sir," Rachel answered.

"Then I think that perhaps she should apologise don't you?"

"Yes sir. I'm sorry that I didn't wish you good morning sir."

The vicar waited a moment or two. Then with obvious surprise he said, "Is that all? Do you not also apologise for pushing past me on the pavement?"

The class listened, hardly daring to breathe as a very red faced Rachel almost whispered:

"No sir."

"No sir," repeated the vicar. "Did I hear you correctly? Did you say 'no sir'?"

"Yes sir," Rachel began in a whisper. But then, with the words almost tumbling out of her mouth, she spoke louder and louder so that the whole class wanted to cheer!

"You see sir, we're chapel and my mother says we mustn't take no notice of church and vicars and that. Besides, a gentleman should step off the pavement for a lady."

The vicar stared at her in astonishment. Finally he exclaimed. "What gross impertinence. Go and stand in the corner and listen very carefully to what I have to say to the class as a whole.

"Now class. It is very important to show proper respect to your elders and betters. We respect our parents and our grandparents because they are older than we are and ought to know better than we do – although *some* parents obviously need to come to school to learn. Soldiers respect their officers and salute them because they wear the king's uniform and represent our country. God is superior even to the king so we show respect to the vicar because he is an officer in God's army and wears God's uniform."

Iris Williams leaned over the gangway to Jimmy Smith and

31

whispered, "D'you know. When he passed Rachel this morning he yanked her back with the crook of his umbrella and he didn't half tell her off. Her dad's a preacher but he don't wear no uniform and we don't have to get off the pavement for him."

"You girl. What are you talking about? Yes you. I'm speaking to you. It's very rude to whisper. Tell the whole class."

"Please sir, I only told Jimmy Smith that Rachel's dad's a preacher."

"That only makes Rachel's crime more serious. She should know the importance of paying respect to the minister of God. Now, let us continue.

"I said that we respect God because he is superior to all of us, even the king. But even more than that, we love him because he loves us. Our parents love us and we love them. God is our heavenly parent. He is our Father and he loves us and we love him."

Jimmy whispered to Roger, "My dad says there ain't no god."

The vicar was growing angry and frustrated. This class wasn't going at all as he had intended.

"You boy. That boy there," and he pointed at Jimmy. "I have already made it clear that it is rude to whisper. What did you say?"

Jimmy stood up and said in a loud voice, "Sir, my dad says there ain't no god."

"Isn't boy, isn't – not ain't. And of course there is a God."

"My dad says there ain't – isn't. He says if there was there wouldn't be no wars and things."

"Then you must tell your father that he is wrong," replied the vicar angrily. "Jesus came to teach us all about God. The Bible is the book which tells us about God. I have studied the Bible. I am God's minister. I know God. I meet him in my prayers and I tell you that God is our heavenly Father. He loves us all."

Jimmy sat down and whispered, "I'd rather believe my dad than 'im, and anyway it's rude to point like he did."

"Shut up you silly fool," Roger answered behind his hand. He's watching."

But the vicar pretended not to notice and continued with his lessons:

"As I was saying. God loves us. How do we know that God loves us?"

32

He paused but there was no answer.

"Oh come now," he said. "We know that God loves us because he is our Father. That's why the Lord's Prayer begins 'Our Father which art in heaven'."

"I bet he doesn't know our words to that prayer," whispered Jimmy.

"Shush," Roger answered and the vicar continued as if nothing was happening.

"Where can we read about God's love?"

Everyone knew the answer but Rachel was still standing in the corner and they weren't going to answer his questions while he was punishing her.

The vicar tried again. "What was the hymn we sang in Assembly?"

Without thinking, Joan Liddell answered, "Please sir, 'Jesus loves me' sir."

"Well done young lady, but how does the hymn continue?"

Helped by a prod from the desk behind Joan realised she was letting the side down and lapsed into silence. The vicar had had enough of this. They weren't going to co-operate so he changed his tactics.

"All of you say after me, 'Jesus loves me, this I know'."

"Jesus loves me, this I know."

"For the Bible tells me so."

"For the Bible tells me so."

"So we know God loves us because the Bible tells us, and everything in the Bible is true."

Jimmy leaned across and whispered to Roger again, "My dad says . . ."

Before he could get any further the vicar almost shouted, "I won't have this whispering. Now what did you say?"

"Nothing sir. You stopped me."

The class began to titter until a glare from the vicar stopped them.

"And what would you have said."

"Please sir, my dad says the Bible is just old stories and things."

The vicar tried hard to be patient. "There *are* stories in the Bible. That is quite right. But the stories all teach us about God. And the Bible is much more than a story book. It is the Word of

God. And that Word of God tells us another way in which we know that God loves us. Listen to what it says:

" 'God so loved the world that he gave his only begotten Son that whosoever believeth in him should not perish but have everlasting life.'

"So we know God loves us because of Jesus. Jesus showed his love for us by dying on the cross for us just as the brave soldiers showed their love for us and for their country by dying for us in the Great War."

Iris Williams burst out crying. The vicar looked at her in astonishment and asked, "What on earth is the matter?"

"Please sir," sobbed Iris. "My daddy's a soldier and I don't want him to die."

Nothing was going right today. The vicar wished he hadn't talked about the war. He tried to comfort Iris.

"For goodness sake don't be so silly. There isn't a war at the moment so there's nothing to worry about is there. Now dry your eyes . . . "

"My dad says there's gonna be a war," whispered Jimmy.

The vicar saw him and his patience finally gave way.

"You boy. Come out here. I suppose you were telling your friend what your dad says."

"Yes sir."

"Well never mind about your dad. Let's concentrate on the lesson shall we? Now. Can you hear me?" and he caught hold of Jimmy's ear and twisted it.

"Yes sir," said Jimmy wincing with the pain.

"Good. Then say after me, 'Jesus loves me. This I know!' "

But Jimmy stayed silent.

The vicar's voice became very quiet and sinister. "You had better do as I say boy. Now, repeat after me: 'Jesus loves me. This I know.' "

"But sir," said Jimmy desperately, "my dad says . . . "

"I don't want to know what your dad says," interrupted the vicar. "He says a great deal too much about things he knows nothing about. Now. Say after me: 'Jesus loves me'."

But Jimmy closed his mouth tight.

By this time the vicar was growing very red in the face. He took a cane out of the desk and said, "For the last time say after me: 'Jesus loves me'."

But Jimmy never said a word. There was nothing for it. The vicar had to punish him now.

"Bend over that chair."

Jimmy bent over the chair and the vicar whacked him once and said:

"Now you *know* that Jesus loves you."

He whacked him a second, third and fourth time and with each whack he said,

"Now you know that Jesus loves you."

Iris Williams, who was still upset because of what he had said about soldiers, burst into tears again whereas Jimmy showed no sign of tears. The vicar gave up.

"Go back to your place – and you little girl, stop crying . . . " at which point the bell rang and the class ended with a short prayer. Thankfully the vicar made his escape. As he left the room he noticed Rachel Pollard still standing in the corner. He felt that he hadn't done very well. And he was right. They hated him.

# 6

# Family Life

The Wallaces lived in a good sized semi-detached house. The front garden was very small but full of roses. It was Mr Wallace's pride and joy.

The front door was recessed under a porch and had stained glass windows with pictures of storks in them. Friends said that was why there were so many children.

Roger never understood that but it seemed to make people laugh no matter how many times they said it. The floor of the porch was tiled with a nice design that went on right through the inside hall and passageway. Stairs ran up from the hall and there were cupboards under the stairs. A coat stand stood inside the door.

To the right was the front room which was usually kept for best. Mostly it was only used on Sundays and for piano practice. But that was the room where Gerry did his Punch and Judy shows for Roger and Margaret. And on Sundays Roger and Margaret were allowed to play in there as long as they were quiet.

Roger liked to set up his farm with all its animals. And then he would put cowboys around and call it a ranch. That led to battles with Indians and sometimes he forgot and got a bit noisy.

"Be quiet boy. It's Sunday. If you're not quiet you'll have to put all those things away."

Lilian wasn't sure whether he ought to be playing with such things on a Sunday. The farm was all right perhaps, but cowboys and Indians didn't seem right somehow.

Roger's battles spread wherever there was space. Up onto

armchairs, with Indians hiding behind cushions to ambush cowboys as they rode past; high on the window ledge with cowboy snipers hiding behind vases to shoot at Indians; even on and under and in the piano.

"Whoosh," a shower of arrows; "bang", a six shooter; "Aaagh", a death.

"That's quite enough of that." George couldn't concentrate on his paper. "You put all those things away and find something quiet to do."

Sadly Roger collected his things together and put them away. It took him ages. He always took a long time over things he didn't want to do. And he didn't always find all the cowboys and Indians he had hidden. It didn't matter much until the piano tuner came. He was a nasty little man who didn't like children, especially children who were so interested in the innards of a piano that they always wanted to watch and get in the way.

If he found cowboys or Indians in the piano he always told Mr Wallace. "They could damage the piano badly, Mr Wallace, and give you a really big repair bill."

They never did but George was always sufficiently troubled by the prospect to make him give Roger a whacking so that he learned not to do it again. Only Roger didn't learn. That's not quite true. He did learn to fear the piano tuner's visits and to hate the man who told on him.

The passage from the front door passed between the stairs and the front room to the dining-room. That led out through French windows into the small garden at the back. The kitchen was next to the dining-room and was another large room with a small scullery behind it where the washing was done, and the washing up after meals.

Mondays were wash days. George lit the copper boiler out in the scullery before he went to work. And as soon as breakfast was over and the boys were off to school, Lilian set to work boiling, bumping and scrubbing until everything was clean. Then everything had to be rinsed thoroughly and there was the starching of collars and cuffs and sometimes of whole shirts.

One Monday when Roger came home for lunch he found his mother with tears streaming down her face, fishing the potatoes out of the copper boiler. She pretended her tears were perspiration. She had dropped a whole saucepan full of potatoes into the boiler.

"You don't need to have any," she screamed at Roger, "but just you keep your mouth shut, that's all. Don't tell the others."

During school holidays the boys often used to help their mother wring the clothes out – twisting the sheets round and round until most of the water was out of them. Then they were folded nicely and put through the mangle to squeeze more water out before they were hung on the line to dry.

Roger enjoyed working with the mangle when he was old enough. But you had to be very careful with shirt buttons or they would break and his mum would have to find a spare from the button box and sew it on. No wonder she took all the buttons off old clothes before turning them into handkerchiefs and table napkins, or using them as rags to patch the children's clothes.

Every time Roger started working the mangle he could guarantee his mother would shout, "Be careful with your fingers mind. Don't forget Auntie."

His Auntie Glad had crushed her fingers because she was talking and not thinking one day when she put a sheet through.

The washing seemed to go on all through the week, drying on the line or in the kitchen, being ironed, aired, mended, put away. It was just like that old song 'Dashing away with the smoothing iron . . . ' But Lilian never complained. She used to say, "Just think what it must have been like for my mother with her five girls and all those petticoats to iron."

During the holidays the boys all had their separate tasks. Roger didn't mind having to clean out the grates and set the fires ready for lighting. But he hated it if he actually had to light them using the gas poker. That thing scared him stiff.

He didn't mind it when he had to Bissell the dining-room floor and brush the table with the crumb tray. And when he was allowed to use the vacuum cleaner he felt quite proud.

But his mother only sent him shopping if there was no one else. He was hopeless. He was for ever leaving the change behind and having to go back to fetch it. All the shopkeepers knew him.

"Been day dreaming again have you Roger? You need to use your head to save your legs."

But Roger liked day dreaming. He especially liked being a cowboy riding his horse, though he sometimes felt a bit daft when he saw people watching him.

Washing up was a job all the boys shared. Eric stood at the sink in the kitchen and washed. Gerry dried. Alfie had the soft job, but he would wouldn't he. He just stood in the doorway between the scullery and the kitchen and caught things when Gerry threw them to him. Then he threw them to Roger who put them away in the kitchen sideboard. If he couldn't reach, Alfie put them away. He did manage to do that.

They never broke a thing – or so they said.

When their jobs were done the boys nearly always went to the park across the road to play football. They were mad on football those Wallace boys. Never did anything else. And they let Roger play. He was much too young and he got in the way, but it was better than looking after him.

If the weather was too bad for the park Mrs Wallace used to go spare. All the children would be in the house. She kept Margaret with her and sent the boys upstairs.

Up the first flight of stairs there was another decent hall surrounded by three double bedrooms, one single bedroom and the bathroom. Another narrow set of stairs led up to the attic which George had turned into a playroom with a named cupboard under the eaves for each of the children.

In the days before it was a playroom, when Roger was just a baby, Alfie and Eric had climbed up into the attic to go exploring. Alfie had slipped off a beam and grabbed Eric to stop himself falling. As a result they both fell straight through the ceiling and down onto the beds below. They weren't hurt but the mess was terrible and they both got a good whacking for that.

But it was their accident that led George to make the attic into a playroom. The boys were supposed to play quiet table games up there. But they only did that when their dad was at home. Mostly they played football.

"You and Eric play me and Roger," said Alfie.

He put Roger in goal his end and Eric chose to go in goal the other end. He liked playing in goal, and anyway it was better than getting hacked by Alfie. *He* played dirty.

So Gerry had to play against Alfie. It wasn't fair. Gerry was four years younger than Alfie and Alfie fouled and tripped and cheated. Up and down the playroom they went, shouting and yelling at one another and making a terrific racket.

"Goal," cried Alfie.

"It wasn't. It went over the top," Eric answered.

"No it didn't. It went right in."

"The goal is here," said Eric carefully marking a small goal all round him.

"That's not fair. That's not nearly big enough. The goal reaches out to here and that was a goal."

"No it wasn't."

"Yes it was."

"It wasn't. You're a cheat."

"Are you calling me a cheat?"

"Well you are a cheat."

Alfie went for Eric but Eric dodged and smacked Alfie hard on the nose – a real good punch. Then he ran for it, out of the attic, clattering down the wooden stairs with Alfie hard on his heels, down to the bedroom landing and down the main stairs, swinging round the bottom of the banisters and along the passageway past the front room, into the back room, round the dining-room table and straight out through the French windows into the garden.

Only the French windows were closed at the time.

Eric wasn't hurt but there was glass everywhere. That evening the four boys were sent down to the garden shed. Inside the shed there was a bunch of bamboo canes. Each boy chose his own cane. They were careful not to choose the thin, whippy ones.

But it was no easy matter walking back to the house with a cane in their hands knowing that their dad had an arm like a blacksmith. Not that they felt badly about the canings themselves. Even at that age, Roger had learned to be quite philosophical about canings.

If he deserved them, that was fair enough. If he was caned unjustly, then he reasoned that he got away with things so often that the odd unjust caning did no more than restore the balance a bit.

But it was hard having to watch the other boys being caned before it was his turn. And his father didn't seem to be taking any notice of the cry from the house:

"Not too hard George. You don't know your own strength."

He might not, but they did. First Alfie, then Eric, then Gerry. This was much worse than when it was just him in trouble. His father turned to him just as his mother shouted again:

"Just be careful George. Not too hard."

George looked at Roger, so much smaller than all the rest. He was scared but trying to be brave and not to cry. It wasn't often that George was deflected from his purpose but . . .

"Let that be a lesson to you. Next time you'll be caned as well. Now. Go and say sorry to your mother, all of you."

Poor Lilian. She was more upset than any of them. She tried not to tell George when they had been naughty, but she could hardly hide the French windows from him could she.

# 7

# Bonfire Night 1937

That autumn Roger went to his first bonfire night party. His mother didn't like fireworks so all they ever had at home was a few sparklers. But Jimmy always had a bonfire party in his garden. He asked Roger if he would like to come with his sister Margaret. She was friends with Jimmy's sister Ruth. So they went.

It was a lovely, crisp, clear evening but they weren't used to being out after dark. They walked round the corner and down the road to the domineering, heavy grey old church. As they passed through the gate to walk the lane through the graveyard, Margaret took hold of Roger's hand.

"I don't like it in here. There's no street lights."

"But there's a good moon shining."

"Yes but it's a bit creepy."

"There's nothing to be afraid of. Look I've got my pistol and my handcuffs."

"You can't frighten skelingtons with pistols."

"The skelingtons – it ain't skelingtons. It's skeletons. – You don't need to worry about them. They're all underground."

"But suppose they was to come up."

"They won't come up. They only do that sort of thing in story books. Besides, look, there's the gate out onto the road again. We'll be at Jimmy and Ruth's house in a minute."

When they arrived they found lots of people in the garden. There were plenty of their friends, Iris and Rachel and some of the boys from school, and Jimmy's father was just about to light the bonfire. Jimmy's guy was sitting on the top.

It was soon burning fiercely, and then they started to let off the fireworks. Jimmy's dad tried to keep some sort of order, but it was a bit of a muddle and soon there were fireworks whizzing and whooshing all over the place. On the trees around the pond there were some Catherine Wheels and Jimmy's mother helped Ruth and Margaret to light them. Some of the boys had squibs. One fell just in front of Rachel Pollard. She was so startled that she tumbled back, bumped into Roger and both of them tumbled into the hedge.

"Get off," he said.

"Give us a kiss first."

"Soppy date. I don't kiss girls."

"Go on."

"No. Get off me."

"I will when you give me a kiss."

"Oh, all right." He pecked her and she got up. "You aren't half heavy," he said.

"No I'm not. You only say that because I made you give me a kiss. And anyway you're a squirt, so there." She left him and joined Iris to boast about getting Roger to kiss her.

As the fireworks ran out and the fire quietened down Mrs Smith and some of the other mothers came out of the house with treacle toffee for everyone. Mr Smith put chestnuts in the fire to roast. They flew about a bit when their shells split, but they tasted nice. And then there was cocoa for all of them and it was time to go home.

A grey mist had come up from the river. It swirled all round them and turned the street lights into small glowing balls surrounded with a blue haze. Roger and Margaret felt frightened. It was well past their bed-time. They held hands and hurried along until they reached the grave-yard.

"Can't we go round?" said Margaret. "It's spooky in there."

"It's a terrible long way if we go round." Roger answered. "We'll go through on tip-toe. Hold my hand tight."

They crept forward, step by step along the path. It would have been better to have run. It took so long. And then a horrible white thing rose up out of the ground groaning and screaming.

They didn't wait to find out what it was. They just turned tail and ran back to Jimmy's house.

"Hello," said Mr Smith, "what are you two doing here?"

"We seen a skelington."

"More like a ghost."

"It groaned and screamed. It was horrible."

Mr Smith laughed and put on his coat. He called to his wife, "Elsie, I'm just going to take the Wallace children home. Old Sam's up to his tricks in the churchyard."

He fetched his bike, put Margaret on the saddle, and he and Roger walked side by side, out they went round the churchyard.

"What you saw wasn't a skeleton or a ghost," he said. "There are no such things as ghosts. What you saw was an old chap who likes a bit of fun."

"Don't think much of his idea of fun," said Roger.

"No I'm sure you don't. But he doesn't mean any harm. Sam's a bit of a rascal and he often gets himself into scrapes but he's all right really. Your dad could tell you a story or two about him, I'm sure."

And with that they were home. Mr Wallace came to the door and was surprised to see Jimmy's dad with them.

"You didn't need to walk them home," he said. "They are old enough to walk on their own."

"They saw old Sam in the churchyard and got scared so I thought I'd better."

"Oh, I see. Been up to his old tricks has he? D'you want to come in for a drink?"

"No thanks George. I'd best get home. Don't want to miss the train in the morning."

"Oh. Right. Thanks for looking after the kids. And thanks for the party. Lilian doesn't like fireworks.

Roger and Margaret were cuddled either side of their dad. Margaret said a shy 'thank you' and Roger also thanked Mr Smith. He swung his leg over the cross-bar and cycled off into the mist. As soon as the door was shut Roger said, "Who is old Sam? Mr Smith said you could tell us lots of stories about him."

"Well maybe I could, but not tonight. Did you enjoy the bonfire party?"

They both talked at once as he packed them off to bed. In moments they were both fast asleep.

# 8

# Old Sam

Saturday was the only day the children really saw their dad. In the afternoons he used to take them all out and give his wife a break. It was easy when the Eagles were at home. Then he took them all to watch the football.

Roger and Margaret climbed up onto the barricades so that they could see better. One Saturday there was a lot of laughter all round. Mr Wallace and the boys couldn't see what was causing their mirth. And then Eric noticed that Margaret's knickers had fallen down and she was showing her bum to everyone.

Mr Wallace took an awful lot of persuading to take her with him after that. The crowd ribbed him something terrible.

But Roger and Margaret soon got bored with the football and went off on their own collecting cigarette cards to play with.

The Saturday evening after bonfire night Roger said, "Who is old Sam, Dad?"

"Sam? Oh he's just a local rascal."

"Yes, but who is he? You promised you would tell us about him."

"Well everybody knows him but nobody knows much about him. They do say as he was the son of the old vicar."

"Now Dad. Be careful what you tell the boy. The old vicar and his housekeeper weren't married remember," Lilian interrupted him.

"Eh. Oh yes, I see what you mean. Well I don't really know where Sam came from. But he used to live in the stables at the old vicarage and do odd jobs about the place — a bit of gardening, repairs, that sort of thing. He can turn his hand to anything can old Sam. And when he works he's a jolly good worker. But he's never had a proper job."

"He's never had a proper home neither, poor devil," said Lilian.

"No. Though I don't know as he's a poor devil. I think he prefers it that way."

"At this time of year, all cold and wet?"

"Why where does he live?" asked Roger.

"That's a good question," said his father. "When the present vicar came they got rid of the old vicarage and old Sam wasn't wanted in the new place. He built himself a shack in some woods over near the new park."

"What, near the new swings?" Roger said.

"Is that what you call them? Yes, that's right. Well then the council cut down all the woods to build a new housing estate so Sam had to move on. I don't know where he lives now."

But Roger had a feeling that he did. He had seen something deep in the woods the day he played truant from school. He persuaded Jimmy to cycle out with him to have a look. They didn't know the woods very well. They were right on the edge of the territory the boys usually covered. And if they went in the woods, they usually rode straight through on the paths or else went down to the lake for a bit of fun.

But on this day they rode beyond the lake and then hid their bikes in the undergrowth a little way off the path. Deep in the woods there was a small area where there seemed to be a lot of bushes growing almost like a rectangular hedge. They made their way towards it, sneaking from tree to tree and watching for any sign of movement. As they drew nearer they realised that there was smoke coming from the centre of the bushes. There must be something there.

Their hearts were thumping now but neither would admit to the other that he was scared. They moved forward more slowly. Roger remembered that awful ghost in the graveyard and wondered what old Sam would do if he caught them snooping around. Jimmy's fear was mixed with excitement. He was more of a dare-devil than Roger. They reached the hedge. It really was a hedge. They edged carefully around it looking for an entrance. They reached the entrance but it overlapped with the other part of the hedge. It had been planted so that you couldn't peer straight in. Cautiously they moved a step or two further so that they could peep around the edge and see what was inside.

Hands fell firmly on their necks and held them fast. Roger felt like a hypnotised rabbit unable to move. But Jimmy wriggled madly to get free. The hand let go his neck and caught his arm.

"Now you two young varmints. What do you think you're up to?"

"We ain't varmints," grunted Jimmy, still struggling hard to get free.

"Please sir," said Roger, "we're looking for old Sam, sir."

"Looking for old Sam is it? Well that's enough of the 'old'. Sam I been and Sam I am. So what do you want Sam for?"

"Sir," said Roger while Jimmy went on struggling. "You frightened me and my sister on bonfire night and Jimmy's dad said it was only a bit of fun and that my dad could tell me things about you. Only my dad didn't tell me much so we thought we'd come and make your acquaintance sir."

"That's a long, posh speech for a little lad. How about coming in for a drop of herb beer then?"

Jimmy stopped struggling and Roger spoke for both of them. "Herb beer sir. Is it . . . Is it like *real* beer sir because if it is I've never had real beer sir. Yes please, we'd like to."

"First of all you've got to make me a promise," said Sam.

"What sort of a promise?" growled Jimmy.

"I can see as you two boys is decent enough. But I likes to keep myself to myself and I don't want no one else coming down here. So you must promise to keep my place secret. If you do, then I'll let you come again. But if you don't, first I shall give you both hell and then I shall disappear."

"What, in a puff of smoke?" asked Roger who was beginning to think that Sam had supernatural powers.

"No stupid. I shall just up sticks and off and find somewhere else to live."

"Oh we don't want to make you do that. Yes, we'll promise."

"On your honour."

"Yes sir. Honest."

"You too young squirmer?"

"Yes," said Jimmy. "Me too. This is too good to share with anyone."

47

Sam let them go and said, "Come on then. We'll seal your promise with a glass of herb beer."

He led the way into his home. It was like a large garden shed. Half way down one side there was an open wood fire, and beside it a cooker made out of two biscuit tins fixed together and coated with a thick coating of mud. It had space for a fire underneath it. Both fires led into a chimney pipe which ran out of the side of the shed and up some feet higher than the roof.

At the further end of that side was the kitchen and washing area, with an old kitchen sink and a drainage pipe leading right out beyond the hedge to a soakaway.

On the wall opposite the kitchen there was a bunk bed and up at the end by the entrance door there was a sitting room with just one chair and a radio, and a little workshop with Sam's bench and his tools and another chair. He obviously sat at his bench to have his meals.

"Gosh," said Jimmy. "You got everything in here. A whole house in this little she . . . place."

"It's amazing," said Roger in wonder. "It really is amazing. And snug too. My mum was worried about you in the wet, cold winter nights."

Sam had poured them mugs of herb beer (but only about half full). "That's kind of your mum. What's she called?"

"Mrs Wallace."

"What Mrs Wallace whose husband owns the factory?"

"Yes."

"Nice people," said Sam. "If ever I'm short of a bob or two I goes to the factory and asks for a bit of work. Your dad always gives me something to keep me going for a few days until I need a rest."

"He said you're good at all sorts of work," said Roger.

"Ah. And who are you young lad?"

"Jimmy Smith. We live . . . "

"Oh I know where you live. You got a sister ain't yer."

"Yes but . . . "

"Your dad comes down my pub. Always good for a laugh he is. And a fair shot with darts too."

"My dad says you used to work for the old vicar," said Roger.

"Yes, good chap."

"But you don't work for the new one."

"Him. Old stiff and starchy, no fear. Wouldn't work for him if he came to me on his bended knees. Nor that sister of his. She's even worse."

"We don't like him either," said Jimmy.

"He's like a stuffed up peacock," said Sam and the boys giggled.

"An' he's got all these fancy new ways in church too, bobbing and bowing and waving smelly stuff around and all that. Not that I been to church since the old vicar died – an' then only because I more or less had to to keep me job."

"What will you do at Christmas?" asked Roger.

"I shall go and spend it with me friends, Constable Willis and his friend June, the barmaid at the Rose and Crown. They always have me for Christmas since the old vicar died. He was a good man that old vicar, but I must say as I 'ave a better Christmas now with June and the Constable than I used to have at the vicarage. What do you think of that herb beer then?"

Both of them had started to drink it straight off and had nearly choked. Now they were sipping it very cautiously.

"It's very nice, thank you sir," lied Roger.

"It isn't half strong," said Jimmy. "Much stronger than dad's Guinness."

"Oh you wait 'til I tell your dad."

"No," said Jimmy hastily. "Don't do that."

"Don't you worry lad. We'm friends now. I shan't drop you into trouble. But talking of trouble, isn't it time you was going home?"

"I dunno. What time is it?"

"Close to tea-time I reckon so you'd best be off."

Roger felt a bit light-headed as they made their way back to their bikes. Sam came with them that far.

"Be sure and come again," he said.

"Yes Mr Sam. We will," and they wobbled off up the lane, but the air soon cleared their heads and Sam proved to be dead right. They were home just in time for tea.

c

# 9

# A Happy New Year

The boys soon felt that finding Sam was the best thing they had ever done. They cycled out into the woods to see him whenever they could.

At Christmas they pinched a few tins of stuff from their mother's larders and some slices of turkey and Christmas pudding and cake and biscuits and took it all to Sam to give him a treat.

He didn't ask any questions. He just took their gifts and thanked them, and shared some of them with the boys when he gave them their drinks of herb beer.

It had been raining for days before Christmas. Roger asked Sam how he managed to keep his fire going when the wood was so wet.

"You gotta be prepared for wet weather when you live like I do," said Sam. "My biggest job is collecting wood and cutting it up. You've seen my log pile outside I daresay."

Roger had. It was big, and all the logs cut to the same size so that the pile looked neat and tidy.

"Now come and look here."

Beside the fire there was a large chest with an old curtain covering it. Sam took the curtain off, lifted the lid, and the boys saw that that too was full of logs.

"That's my dry store," said Sam.

"And those are drying off ready to go into the dry store are they?" Jimmy pointed to the logs arranged all around the fire and the cooker, a bit like a fender round a hearth.

"That's right. And in here," Sam opened the oven door, "is my kindling wood all nice and dry. So the rain doesn't bother me."

"What do you do for lights?" asked Jimmy.

"I don't use lights much," said Sam. "Mostly I'm at the Rose and Crown when it's dark or else in bed. But I've got an oil lamp and the front light from my bike."

"And where do you get your food?" asked Roger. "Do you go to the shops like everyone else?"

"I *do* go to the shops, yes, when I've a call to. But mostly I just lives off the land."

"How do you do that?"

"Well it isn't much use me telling you is it. I reckon I'd better show you so's you can learn for yourselves."

So began a number of trips out with Sam that carried them well into 1938. He took them down to the lake fishing.

"You gotta be a bit careful where you go fishing. There's a lot of places that's private so you have to find secret ways to the water and only fish after dark. And there's times of year when fishing's not allowed. You have to get to know all about that."

"But isn't it against the law fishing where it's private?" asked Roger.

"The laws wasn't made for people like me," said Sam, "so I don't always think I need to keep them."

Roger vaguely felt that there must be an answer to that, but he didn't know what it was, and anyway he was on Sam's side whatever the law said.

Sam introduced them to his ferrets. They had never seen ferrets before. He taught them how to hold them. They put them in a sack and he took some nets and out they went catching rabbits.

"A lot of people in my position put snares out for rabbits," said Sam. "But I don't like snares. They can cause a lot of pain. So I just use me ferrets."

He showed them how to skin and clean the rabbits. Roger was too squeamish but Jimmy loved doing it.

"You come for lunch tomorrow and I'll cook you rabbit pie."

They couldn't tell their mums they were going for a meal with Sam. They'd never have been allowed. But they hit on a plan. Each of them asked:

"Can I have some sandwiches tomorrow, Mum."

"Why do you want sandwiches?" Roger's mum asked.

"Me and Jimmy's going down by the lake fishing."

"But you haven't got any fishing tackle."

"We've got some string and we can make hooks with bent pins."

"What about bait?" she asked with a smile.

"We can find some worms I expect, or use the crumbs from our sandwiches."

"There won't be many crumbs left if I know you two."

Jimmy's mum didn't even bother to ask. She was just happy to have him out of the way for the day.

They got to Sam's in time to watch him do his cooking. He showed them how to make pastry and then how to make the pie with the meat all taken off the bones.

"What about vegetables," asked Roger. "Do you get those from the shops?"

"No need is there. All you gotta do is to learn what's in season at any time of year and where to find it. Sometimes I gets things from the fields and sometimes from the allotments."

"But that's pinching," said Roger wide-eyed.

"Not really," said Sam. "People always sow more than they need and then they don't know what to do with things when they harvest them."

"That's true," said Jimmy. "My dad's always giving stuff away, and he usually ends up having to throw some of it."

"So you see, I'm just helping out really."

Roger wasn't quite convinced but he didn't let it stop him enjoying his meal. He'd never tasted rabbit pie like it and the gravy was wonderful.

"How d'you get such smashing gravy?" he asked. "My mum's is never as good as this."

"Never throw anything away. That's the secret. I 'ad a pheasant a few days ago and then Juney give me a leg of lamb, so there's a bit of pheasant gravy and a bit of lamb gravy all in that together."

"It's super," said Roger.

"June works at the pub doesn't she?" asked Jimmy. "She's my dad's favourite."

"Ah. She would be. She's favourite with a lot of people, specially constable Willis and me," said Sam.

"My mum doesn't like her very much," said Jimmy.

52

"Ah," said Sam and changed the subject.

It was perhaps because Sam became so much a part of their lives that they started to hear different bits and pieces about him. The first time was just after the new year. It was Jimmy's dad who passed the story on.

Every new year's eve Sam went to the pub and afterwards he went home with June for a bit to see the new year in.

He was so happy when he left June's that he used to sing all the way home, and he didn't have a bad tenor voice. People grew accustomed to it, even looked forward to it.

When the old vicar was alive, Sam used to go from June's straight – well, perhaps straight is not quite the right word – to the vicarage to wish the vicar a happy new year. And the old vicar used to give him a hug and a couple of quid and send him off to bed with his blessing.

Sam had never gone to the new vicarage. But this year he was feeling friends with everybody. He must go and make friends with this new vicar, even with his sister if he had to. He sang his way to the new vicarage and knocked on the door.

It was two o'clock in the morning and there was no response. He continued to sing, put one finger on the bell and held it there while he used the other hand to knock. Pretty good to be able to do three things at once at two o'clock on New Year's morning.

At long last the vicar appeared in his dressing gown with his sister standing behind him.

"Happy New Year vicar. Peace on earth though not for much longer if that bloody Hitler has his way. Goodwill to all men. Shall I sing you a song Vicar?"

"You're drunk. Go away and stop disturbing decent folks."

"Now, Vicar, that's no way to speak to a friend who just wants to wish you and your sister there a happy new year."

"For goodness sake keep your voice down. You'll disturb the whole neighbourhood."

His sister was on the phone. It was a long time before anyone answered.

"Constable. Come at once. The new vicarage. There's a horrible man here who is drunk and disorderly. He needs a night in the cells to sober him up."

Constable Willis promised to come and put the phone down.

"Danged telephones. They'd been better off without them," he thought.

"What is it Harry?" asked his wife Emily sleepily.

"It's the vicar and his sister. They want me to arrest old Sam for disturbing them. I shall have to spend the night at the station with him in the lock up. That's a right 'happy new year' isn't it."

"Never mind dear. It could be worse. Sam won't give you no trouble."

"It could be a lot worse," thought the constable. He pulled on his boots, took his cycle and rode round to the vicarage.

Sam had at last got the message that he was not welcome. He was walking down the road singing his heart out. The constable got off his bike and took Sam by the arm. He managed to stop the singing by keeping Sam talking. Before long they found themselves outside June's house again. Sam insisted on wishing her a happy new year once more, so the constable parked his bike alongside the house and the two of them made their way to the front door.

June had seen them coming and whisked them inside. Harry explained that they were on the way to the police station and would be spending the night there.

"You can't do that Harry. Not on new year's morning. I don't know what you're thinking of. Look Sam's almost asleep already. Come on, give me a hand with him."

With much giggling and heaving they managed to get Sam up the narrow staircase to June's bedroom. They took off his clothes and pushed him into her bed.

"There," she said. "We'll get him up nice and early in the morning, put a good breakfast inside him and have him down at the cells before anyone else is around."

"You're ever so decent to him," said Harry.

"Now. What about you? I suppose because you've arrested him you've got to stay with him."

"Well, I should really."

"Then you might as well get your clothes off and get in beside him. I'll see you're up in time in the morning."

"But what about you?"

"Oh, don't worry about me. I can soon find myself somewhere to sleep. Now. Get a move on and get into that bed."

So Harry stripped off and climbed into bed beside Sam. It was a big double bed so there was plenty of room. There was still enough room when June showed Harry what she meant by finding herself somewhere to sleep. He began to feel that the vicar had done him quite a favour really.

In fact before he went to sleep he felt that the vicar had given him the best new year's morning of his life. And the fact that the night was rather short didn't seem to matter.

June was as bright as a button and cooked them a splendid breakfast and then the two of them hurried down to the station and Harry locked Sam into the cell. They were only just in time.

The vicar arrived to press his charges. In due course the magistrates bound Sam over to keep the peace. That was what they normally did when Sam came before them. They were going to make it twelve months, but then they realised that that might spoil his next Christmas and New Year so they made it nine months instead. They knew Sam too well to imagine that he would ever change, and he was harmless for goodness' sake.

# 10

# The May Fayre

Through what was left of the Christmas holidays and then through the Easter holidays, Roger and Jimmy spent as much time as they could at Sam's place. And he never seemed to mind – actually seemed to enjoy their company and their admiration.

He kept out of trouble. June and Constable Willis saw to that. If it hadn't been for the vicar's reaction to the May Fayre, Sam might have kept out of the lime-light altogether.

No one knew how long there had been a May Fayre. When it started there must just have been a small village there. Although the village had long since been swallowed up by new housing estates where people had no sense of community at all, it had clung on to something of its old identity. And so the fayre lived on, although everything took place in the somewhat artificial setting of Central Park now.

For months before the fayre, women in the village and mothers of the school-children were busy making decorations for the floats and fancy dress clothes for themselves and the children. Local businesses joined in and provided floats of their own. The school was busy getting the maypole ready and teaching the children the maypole dances. In the village hall the Morris dancers got together once a week for their practices before going down to the pub to make it all worthwhile.

But mostly the men kept out of the way until it was time to decorate the lorries and the great shire horses and their carts ready for the grand procession.

The school had decided to do a tableau of Robin Hood and his merry men. Roger felt quite proud when he was chosen to be Robin Hood, but he wasn't so pleased when Joan Liddell was chosen as Maid Marion. She was too goodie-goodie. He would have liked freckle-faced Rachel Pollard. She was much more fun. Jimmy was Will Scarlet.

May Day came and the lorries and horses and carts all converged on the school. The children in the tableau made their way to the cart decked out as part of the greenwood.

They climbed into their places. Will Scarlet took his lyre. He felt a bit wet. He'd far rather have had a bow and arrows. Robin had those and Maid Marion wore the same outfit the school had used for Mary in the Nativity Play at Christmas.

The local brass band led the procession out of the school gates and off towards the High Street. The horse dropped a huge dollop of manure in the road. "Cor," said Will Scarlet. I wish we was on a lorry. What a horrible stink."

Behind the school the Boys Brigade band was doing its best to drown out the sounds of the village band up ahead. Still further back a police band brought up the rear. Anyone who could hear all three was in real trouble. So was the police drum major. Keeping his eye on his swirling stick he failed to notice the horse manure and walked straight into it.

Up the High Street they went, down Bridge Street and over the river out to the park. The horse really had enjoyed his oats that morning. He farted merrily all the way over the bridge. Will Scarlet had had enough. "Pwaw. 'Ere, Little John swap places with me for a bit. This 'orse pongs horrid. 'E never stops farting."

For a little while Robin Hood and his merry men really were pretty merry. They found it almost impossible to stand still and statuesque when Lord and Lady Croy walked up and down the line of floats judging which was the best. But they must have done pretty well because their horse wore the rosette for best tableau.

There were a couple of speeches. Then Lord and Lady Croy went off to the marquee to judge the flower and vegetable displays and the cookery and everyone else went off to enjoy themselves. There were races. There were all kinds of stalls raising money for different organisations in the village. And there was the fair proper with swings and roundabouts and Madame Fortune and bumper cars and – oh, all the usual things.

It was a wonderful day, one of the high points of the year. The fair continued well into the evening and inevitably it ended up with a few friendly fights when the men had got a bit of drink in them, but there was nothing serious. The serious work was going on in darker parts of the park. The village always had a rather high birth-rate in February.

Out of all the day's events it was typical that the vicar should focus on those two things in his Sunday sermon. He ranted and raved about the disgraceful moral standards of the village. He called for a return to the old ideals and standards. He really went to town, with his sister nodding furiously in support in the front pew.

The following Thursday the sermon was splashed across the front page of the *Echo*: 'Vicar slams village morals.'

A week later there was another front page note advising people to 'see the letters page for reaction to the vicar's sermon reported last week.'

Even though it had been front page news, very few people had bothered to read the sermon. The headline was enough. But they did read the letters. Under the caption 'Letter Of the Week' they read:

Dear Sir,

I am so glad that at long last we have a vicar who is concerned about the morality of the people of this village. There is nothing we need more than high moral standards.

May I humbly suggest to the vicar that there is one way in which he and his sister could raise the moral standards of the people immediately.

They could buy some bathroom curtains.

Yours sincerely,

Mr S. Woodman.

The letter had the desired effect. Not only was there great merriment throughout the village but new curtains also appeared in the vicarage bathroom. And even though 'Woodman' was not Sam's real surname, most people seemed to assume that he was the one who had written the letter. Yet Sam couldn't write, apart from signing his name, so someone must have helped him. The signature was certainly his.

Both June and Constable Willis enjoyed everyone's merriment, but neither of them was very forthcoming when people asked questions about Mr Woodman.

# 11

# A Mighty Splash

Spring turned to summer and summer to autumn and the village whist drives began again. With high glee Maud and Mildred returned to the fray. They were both ninety, born on the same day, best of friends and oldest of rivals. Both of them were good at cards and each was determined to out-live the other.

It was entirely fitting that, while they were arguing with some heat about who had played the ace of clubs five hands ago, they should both have massive heart attacks, throw their cards in the air and drop dead.

But which of them had gone first? After much debate the villagers decided that it was a dead heat. Everybody in the village agreed that they must have a double funeral and be laid to rest in adjoining graves – everybody that is, except their two families.

They met in the village hall with half the village standing around to see fair play and cut a pack of cards to see who should be buried first. Maud's family lost. But the families did agree on adjoining graves, so the sexton got to work.

The churchyard had been used several times before so the soil had never had too long to settle. That meant that digging the graves wasn't too difficult. The vicar kept coming out to make sure that he didn't disturb those who had been buried before. He was allowed to go down five feet and no more. At five shillings a grave he felt quite wealthy. He'd have a good celebration that night for certain.

So, on a beautiful October morning Maud was laid to rest.

Everybody in the village was there (except Mildred of course), even Constable Willis and Sam. There were masses of floral tributes which reminded Sam or something he had noticed on his way home every night after a funeral.

As soon as the funeral was decently over and they were all back at the pub celebrating Maud's life, it began to rain – real, hard October rain. It was obvious to all of them that Maud was not pleased that Mildred had been allowed an extra day above ground.

"Mildred's grave'll be three inches deep in water if this goes on all night."

"Six inches, more like, and all that clay will be some mess."

The rain did continue non-stop. Mildred's family began to wish they had agreed to a double funeral. The night was black as pitch. So when Sam set off for home through the grave-yard he was astonished to see a lantern by Maud's grave. He couldn't believe it.

"Even on a night like this," he said to himself. "She must be mad."

It was the vicar's sister who had braved the elements. She had gathered a fine bouquet of flowers carefully taken from each of the tributes so that no one would notice the loss.

Sam had moved quietly through the grave-yard to be quite sure. He was impressed, and not just by her determined thrift or her bouquet. No. On this sombre occasion, as she bent before him he was impressed by the magnificent proportions of her black-skirted, black-coated bottom. He was irresistibly drawn towards it. Moving silently forward he gave it the very gentlest of shoves.

With a terrible shriek and the flowers of her bouquet flying in all directions, she fell with a mighty splash into the clay-stained waters at the bottom of Mildred's empty grave.

Sam grabbed her lantern and went on a merry dance all over the grave-yard before returning it to a spot where it would light the top of the grave.

Now it just so happened that the sexton had gone from the pub to the home of Emily Willis, the constable's wife. After a long and lingering farewell he was now hurrying home to his own. He heard the shriek and saw a light flying about all over the grave-yard. In terror he ran to fetch the vicar. Unfortunately for him, Sam saw him go.

The vicar, thinking that his sister was safely tucked up in bed, had just poured himself a particularly large whisky. In answer to the sexton's endless knocking he came to the door with his glass in his hand.

"Oh, thank you," cried the sexton, taking the glass and knocking back the whisky. "You must come at once vicar. Maud's got free of her grave. She's dancing all over the grave-yard."

"Don't be silly man. You've been drinking," answered the vicar taking his glass back in dismay. But as he stood in the open doorway more screams rent the night air.

"There," said the sexton, "hear that? You must come and do an exorcism or something."

The vicar went indoors to get his boots and his coat. And while he was about it he fortified himself with a good stiff whisky to make up for the one he had lost and to help him to face whatever it was in the grave-yard.

Meanwhile Sam had run to June's house to dig out P.C. Willis whose nightly beat always seemed to include a long stop there.

"You'd better come quick Harry. There's something funny going on in the grave-yard."

While Harry was struggling back into his uniform, Sam whispered to June that even on such a filthy night anyone who saw what was happening might enjoy a treat.

Sam and Harry set off for the grave-yard and June got busy rounding up a few friends before following them. As the two men reached the gateway, in the light of the grave-side lamp they saw a ghostly face emerge briefly from Maud's grave before falling back with a cry of despair into the bottom of the grave again.

P.C. Willis was not an imaginative man but he didn't like what he saw.

Again that dreadful clay-covered face rose white in the dim light of the lamp and fell back with an awesome groan. Then they caught sight of another light and two black-coated figures moving silently towards the grave.

"You go round that way Harry and I'll come at them from behind. We'll soon discover what they are up to."

P.C. Willis was not too keen. He moved very slowly to take up his position which gave Sam all the time he needed. Swiftly and silently he came up behind the vicar and the sexton. He stooped and cupped a hand around the sexton's foot.

The sexton fell and the lamp flew out of his hand and went out. As he fell he grabbed at the vicar's cloak. It took very little help from Sam to ensure that he fell too.

As the two men tried to disentangle themselves it almost seemed to them as though there were three people all mixed up, so many arms and legs were flailing around. The vicar caught a fist in the eye. The sexton felt a boot rather firmly where it hurts most. Both of them had their faces rubbed in the mud so that by the time they were on their feet again they were both very uncomfortable and very angry with one another.

By this time Harry was approaching with considerable caution. When Sam suddenly appeared at his elbow he was more than a little startled.

"It's just a couple of old drunks having a fight," said Sam. "You'd better take them to the cells to cool off, and that woman practising witchcraft in Mildred's grave too."

By now P.C. Willis was close enough to the two men to see who they were. He turned to Sam, "I can't arrest *them*," he whispered.

"Hush," said Sam. "Give me the lamp. Then you can't see who they are. Just take them away at least as far as the road. June deserves to get a sight of your bravery, arresting such varmints."

"June?"

"She'll be there I promise you. That witch has fair disturbed all the neighbourhood."

"She won't be there."

"Oh yes she will."

They helped the 'witch' out of the grave, letting her fall just once more for good measure. Then the constable arrested the three of them and set off for the police station through the main gate of the grave-yard. They were in such a state that they went along with him without a word.

Sam slipped quietly out to the road where June and a few friends were waiting in the rain. As P.C. Willis appeared with his three criminals they all passed under a street light.

"Why," shouted Sam, "it's the vicar and the sexton drunk and fighting in the grave-yard but who is that old witch with them?"

"The vicar?" said the constable with unconvincing surprise. "Why, so it is. And you James Harrison. Fancy you fighting with your vicar. And you Miss, just look at the state of you. I can't imagine what you could all have been doing at this time of night frightening decent people out of their wits. You'd better be off home before I take you in and charge you."

"The vicar's got a proper shiner," said Sam. "I didn't know James had it in him. We'll have to watch our step when he's in drink."

The three of them hurried away and June took the little crowd of watchers to the back entrance of the pub for a final warm up before wending their way home. P.C. Willis didn't seem to notice that it was after hours.

It was the vicar of the neighbouring parish who conducted Mildred's funeral. And when the bishop heard a rather garbled account of the things that had happened he decided that some sick leave should be followed by a transfer. It was probably as well. There had been murmurings from that parish ever since this vicar had been installed. Besides his housekeeper's son had just been ordained. This would make a decent first parish for him.

October was followed as usual by November and then December and the school holidays. Roger and Jimmy cycled out to see Sam. They hid their bikes in the usual bramble patch and walked to the hedge – more a thicket than a hedge. They walked inside and there was nothing there. No shed. No log pile. No ferrets. Above all, no Sam. Nothing.

They hurried back to their bikes and cycled straight to June's house.

"Miss June," they chimed. "We've just been to see Sam and he's disappeared. So has his house. Everything. It's all gone."

She looked at them and at their distress. How could she tell them?

"You'd better come in boys."

They followed her into her cosy sitting-room.

"Sit down. I'll get you a glass of Sam's herb beer."

She brought them their drinks and studied them.

"How good are you at keeping secrets?"

They looked at one another.

"We can keep a secret," said Jimmy.

"Sam thought a lot of you two," she said, "so perhaps it will be all right if I tell you but you must promise not to tell."

"We promise Miss," said Roger.

"Don't call me Miss. I'm June."

63

"Yes Miss June," said Roger earnestly.

She smiled. "Come and have a look out of the window."

They looked down her garden. At the bottom of the garden there was a large shed.

"That's like Sam's shed," said Jimmy.

"And you've got a pile of logs just like . . . He's here isn't he?" Roger was so excited.

"No he's not here. He's just left his things for me and he's gone. If ever he comes back, the shed will be here for him."

"But where's he gone?" asked Roger.

"That's something I'm not going to tell you. He's gone to stay with a friend of Harry Willis. It's a long, long way from here."

"By why?" said Jimmy. "He's so popular here. Everyone likes Sam."

June laughed. "Not quite everyone," she said. "He's been accused of something he didn't do. Do you remember that robbery a couple of weeks back at the shop next to Woolworths?"

"Yes."

"Well Sam wasn't far away when it happened and people are saying he did it. P.C. Willis knows he didn't and so do I. Sam wouldn't do a thing like that. But the constable was told to go and arrest him, so he sent me to warn him.

I hid him here and then the next few nights he moved everything he had here to my garden. Then he left. Harry's friend is another policeman. He's found Sam a job on a farm and a farm cottage to live in. Sam is taking the place of a man who has joined the army. If he'll stick to it, it should be just right for him. But he's not used to a regular job so we'll have to wait and see."

"If Mr Willis catches the real thieves, will Sam come back home again?"

"I just don't know. These are funny times what with all this talk about war and things."

"Do you think there will be a war Miss June?" asked Roger.

"It's no use asking me," she laughed. "Mr Chamberlain said there wasn't going to be a war so there probably will be. Politicians usually get it all wrong."

"And they are digging all those trenches aren't they," said Jimmy, "and air-raid shelters and making places for anti-aircraft guns."

"Well that'll give you something else to watch and visit now that Sam's gone," answered June. "You'd better be off. It's time I was getting ready to go to the pub."

"Thank you for telling us," said Roger.

"Well you just be sure and tell no one else."

And strangely enough, they never did.

# 12
# Christmas

Changes *were* taking place. It was in the park that Roger noticed them most. A trench was dug all round the edge of the park and a building that people said was an aid-raid shelter went up. Anti-aircraft gun emplacements began to appear and sites for barrage balloons, all of them surrounded with sand-bags. And there seemed to be soldiers all over the place. Roger had never noticed so many soldiers before.

When they went out into the country he saw concrete pill boxes and tank traps and barbed wire. All of them marked the beginnings of preparations in case of war and a possible enemy bombing campaign or invasion.

But as Christmas drew near Roger forgot all about soldiers and guns and such things. He wrote out his Christmas list and put it in the bedroom fireplace for Father Christmas and he helped both his mother and his grandmother with their Christmas preparations.

He watched them chop the suet and the peel and he helped take the stones out of the raisins. When the pudding mixture was ready he helped to stir it. It took both hands and he didn't get on very well, but his grandmother was always encouraging. She made about twelve Christmas puddings, some of them for giving away to poorer families, and she cooked them (four at a time) in the wash boiler.

In the evenings Roger and Margaret sat on the kitchen floor with pots of glue and lots of loops of coloured paper and they made paper chains for the Christmas decorations. Carol singers came and went and at school it was time for Nativity plays and for the end of term presents.

Each boy and girl had to wrap up one of their personal possessions to give away. Then the teacher started to go round the class starting with the front desks:

"Who would like the present given by . . . "

Hands would shoot up and the teacher would call the name of the person with the first hand. Once you had a present you stopped putting your hand up.

Roger's greatest enemy in the class was Harold Brow. They both wanted Rachel for their girlfriend, and she was perfectly happy to have both of them, and anybody else too. Roger waited until the teacher said:

"Who would like the present given by Harold Brow?"

Up shot his hand and Harold's present was his. It was a pencil box and Roger was quite pleased with it. Harold was determined to get his own back, so he waited.

But Roger had already warned Jimmy Smith not to try to get his present. "Just watch Harold's face if he does," he had said.

At long last Miss Smythe reached the back row and came to Roger's desk.

"Who would like the present given by Roger Wallace?"

Most people had already got their presents, so there weren't many hands to go up. Harold's hand was easily the first. He came and took his present from Roger, gloating. He'd got his own back on Roger Wallace all right.

"Say thank you to Roger," said Miss Smythe. She had insisted on each of the children saying 'thank you'.

Harold managed a grudging "thank you" and returned to his seat to open his present. Roger and Jimmy watched eagerly. Off came the paper and Harold's face dropped. Roger had given him a Bible.

"What a nice present," said Miss Smythe, blissfully unaware of the enmity between the two boys. She completed the present giving and then it was end of term. Roger and Jimmy felt that it had been a good end of term for them.

Holidays meant clothes shopping, putting up decorations and counting the days. But at last Christmas Eve came. In the kitchen they prepared a tray with mince pies and a drink for Father Christmas. And then they tied the huge Christmas stockings their grandma had made to the bottom of their beds. Once in bed they tried very hard to stay awake until after Father Christmas had come, but they fell asleep long before that.

When they woke early on Christmas morning, their sacks bulged nicely at the bottom. They were far from full but the children didn't expect that they would be. There was an apple and an orange (Christmas was the only time they had oranges, but Roger didn't like them anyway). Oh no. There was another orange – or was it?

Roger looked more closely and found it much more to his liking. It was a trick orange. You could fill it with water, offer it to someone and then squirt the water like a water pistol. That really *was* a decent Christmas present. There were a couple of other little things and a book. Christmas always seemed to promise so much and deliver so little. Every year it came as an anticlimax and left him disappointed.

The four boys and Margaret all got together to see what each had received and to do a little bit of swapping and then it was time to wash and go down and have breakfast.

After breakfast had been cleared away and all the washing up finished, Mr Wallace led a procession to the front room. The door was locked and he pretended to have lost the key. When he finally unlocked the door there were seven small groups of parcels – one for each of them.

Roger had got all excited again but as he opened his parcels his disappointment returned. There were two pairs of socks, a vest and a shirt and – at last – a game of Ludo. The others had similar sets of parcels. Alfie, Eric and Jerry had to share their game because it was expensive. They had Monopoly.

By the time their presents had been opened it was time to put on their best clothes and walk about a mile to their grandma's house. It was her turn for Christmas dinner. With all their uncles and aunts and cousins there were twenty-two of them at the dinner table.

Grandpa carved the turkey and when he arrived at the wishbone there was a great fuss about who should pull it. Eric and cousin Paula pulled it and Paula ended up with the bigger bit so she got to wish. They all tried to persuade her to tell what she had wished.

"Just whisper," said uncle Herbert.

"Whispering in company is rude," answered Paula.

"Oh, go on. Just this once."

"If I tell and don't keep it a secret, I shan't get what I wished for. So I won't tell," she said — and she wouldn't either, not to anybody.

As the children ate their pudding each of them found a silver threepenny piece. Suddenly Uncle Jack began to cough and splutter and choke, so badly that he fell off his chair.

Auntie Norah cried, "What ever is the matter?"

In a hoarse voice he cried, "I've swallowed a threepenny bit."

All the adults knew that wasn't true because only the children had them. Grandma used to keep some in her pinny and slip them in whenever she served one of the children. But Uncle Jack put on a great act.

"Water," he cried. "Help. Help." His voice faded. "Give me some water."

Grandpa brought the jug of water and poured some over uncle Jack's head. He spluttered and coughed and made a miraculous recovery while everyone roared with laughter.

Grandpa put the jug back on the table, looked to see that everyone had finished eating, and then cried, "Roger. The humbugs."

Whenever the family had lunch with Grandpa and Grandma there were always humbugs. So Roger fetched them and offered one each to all the girls and ladies. Uncle Jack tried to grab one but Roger was too quick for him.

Then he started on the rounds of the boys and men. This time it was Uncle Herbert who tried to take more than one but Roger snatched it away.

"We're only allowed one each."

"It's Christmas."

"So it may be but you only have one. That's the rule. It's one each or none at all."

He felt quite brave talking to his uncle like that, but that was what his grandpa had said and everyone was cheering him:

"Well done Roger."

"You tell him."

"Naughty man."

With Christmas dinner over, the men took all the children out for a long walk while the women cleared away, washed up and set the tea table. By the time the walkers got back it was time for tea.

First a slice of bread and butter. That was compulsory. Then more bread and butter (with jam this time if you liked), or sandwiches or scones. Then there was jelly or blancmange – one or the other, not both. Finally there was grandma's Christmas cake. It was very rich and Roger was already feeling very full and a bit sick. He didn't really like Christmas cake and he certainly didn't feel like eating any more, but Christmas cake was also compulsory. He struggled through his piece and began to feel pretty awful.

Soon it was time for him and for Margaret, as the two youngest, to set off on the mile long walk home with their mother. They put on their scarves, coats, hats and gloves. By the time they were ready, their aunts and uncles were all in a line from their grandparents ready to say good-bye.

Margaret had to kiss them all, but she didn't seem to mind. Roger shook hands with each of the men but he had to kiss his grandma and his aunts. He didn't mind that usually except for Aunt Henrietta. Like all the rest, she was short and dumpy with big bosoms. All the others kept theirs well covered up, but her's billowed above her clothes in two white masses.

As Roger went down the line (he really was feeling awful), each of the aunts offered him a cheek to kiss until he got to aunt Henrietta.

"You dear little boy," she said and she clasped him to herself.

His head was squashed in against her bosom. He couldn't breathe. He suddenly felt terribly hot. He couldn't – oh gosh – disaster. A rich, gooey mess of Christmas cake, blancmange, sandwiches, Christmas pudding and turkey welled up and he was sick all down his aunt.

She fled.

Grandma quietly took Roger and cleaned him up.

"Never you mind," she said comfortingly. "It wasn't your fault. It was probably my Christmas cake that did it. Here, put this in your pocket to eat when you are feeling better. But don't tell anyone. It's our secret."

And with that she hurried him back out to his mother and to Margaret. His father was all set to tick him off and make him apologise but Grandma got in first:

"George," she said, "don't you dare to say a word to the boy.

It wasn't his fault and I don't want his Christmas spoiled."

No one ever argued with Grandma, so Roger and Margaret set off for home with their mother, and the fresh air soon made Roger feel better. On the way home he tried to make out what it was that his grandmother had given him. It was a tin, but he dared not look to see what sort of tin.

They got home, hung up their hats, coats and scarves and then Roger had some bread and milk because his mother thought he might be hungry after being so sick. And then they were packed off to bed.

After his mother had tucked him in and kissed him 'Good night', he crept out onto the landing and watched until he was sure that she was safely busy in the kitchen. Then as silently as he could he made his way downstairs and slipped into the cupboard where his coat was. It was pitch dark. He felt carefully among the coats until he found his own. Very carefully he eased the tin out of his pocket, opened the cupboard door, and then, quick as a flash, rushed back up the stairs to his bedroom. Only then did he look at his tin.

Grandma had given him the rest of the tin of humbugs. He sneaked out of his bedroom again and up to the playroom in the attic. There, he hid the humbugs in his toy cupboard after taking one for himself. He reckoned that was his best Christmas present – and he had a bit of a giggle when he thought about Aunt Henrietta.

Boxing day saw the same twenty-two sit down to dinner at the Wallaces house with more eating and more walking. Roger managed to say a secret thank you to his grandma but she made light of it.

After tea, there was a tap on the window from outside. They opened the curtain and there was Father Christmas. Amidst a great deal of excitement Roger's dad let him in and helped him with his sack. A chair was set for him to rest in after his long journey and then, with a great deal of ho-ho-ho-ing he started to burrow down into his sack to see if he could find anything for the children. Out came a present for Roger. Father Christmas called him forward. He wasn't altogether sure. He wanted the present, but Father Christmas in all that get up, with that huge white beard, was a bit intimidating. The pull of the present won, Roger took it, said "thank you" and then stopped dead in his tracks.

He turned to his mother and said in a loud voice:

"Why has Father Christmas got Auntie Glad's shoes on?"

He was quickly hushed up and told to open his present, but Margaret hadn't noticed. She was too busy with her present so Roger's observation passed. He opened his present and found that he had got a yo-yo. He was quite pleased about that.

Christmas games followed but before long it was time for Roger and Margaret to be sent up to bed. As the duty kisses were being given, Auntie Henrietta slipped out to the toilet so she didn't get a kiss. The adults were quite amused and Roger was quite relieved that she wasn't there.

# 13

# Evacuees

Back at school gas masks were issued to all the children. Miss Smythe showed them how to put them on. They all tried.

Iris Williams had no sooner got hers on than she took it off again. "Please Miss, it's horrible. And it smells."

"You're quite right Iris. They are horrible and they do smell. That's the rubber. But if Hitler drops gas bombs on us, those masks will save our lives. So put it on again and persevere. There, that's a motto for you: 'Put it on and persevere.' "

Iris put her mask back on. Miss Smythe spoke to them with her mask on. She sounded very funny. Come to that she looked very funny too.

"Deep breaths children. After me, one, two, three, breathe in. Breathe out. Breathe in. Breathe out. Now you can take your masks off."

Thank goodness for that. It was so hot inside and misty. Miss Smythe drew a wavy line on the blackboard, up and down, up and down. Underneath it she drew a straight line.

"Now," she said. "We have got to learn to carry our gas masks wherever we go, all the time, indoors and out of doors. And if we hear an air-raid siren it will sound like this." She pointed to the wavy line and sang up and down, up and down.

"All of you try to be air-raid sirens – no Jimmy, all at the same time, after three: one, two, three."

The noise was awful.

"Stop." She cut them off with a wave and they stopped.

When we hear an air-raid siren, we put our gas mask over our

73

d

shoulder, take our hats and coats and walk in an orderly line to the air-raid shelter. So, let's have the siren again. One, two, three."

Again the children sang out.

"Stop," she commanded. "And now: gas masks. Good. Hats and coats and stand in line. Now follow me."

She led them out and across the quad to the playing field.

"Stop." The aeroplanes have got here before we have had time to get to the shelter. So we shall have to take shelter in the trench. What a good thing we brought hats and coats to keep warm. Follow the leader into the trench quickly and calmly."

They all went down into the trench.

"Well done. Now did anybody notice something on the board beneath the air-raid siren?"

Everybody seemed to have noticed. A chorus of "Please Miss, a straight line Miss."

"Well done. Yes, a straight line like this." And she sang all on one note. "All of you do it." One, two, three."

Singing on one note sounded much better.

"That is the 'All Clear'. It tells us when it is safe to go back to our classroom. Let's have it again: one, two, three."

Again the single note rang out.

"Well done. Last boy into the trench lead the class back to the classroom."

Throughout the spring and summer terms the practice sessions went on, sometimes just with their own class, sometimes with the whole school. And they wore gas masks for longer and longer sessions until they had worn them for a whole class.

And then it was time for summer holidays, the family holiday in Bognor, the declaration of war and the return to school. Blackouts went up at night so that no light came from their houses to the outside world. Street lights went out. Car headlights were masked but for a whole month school went on as usual. Well over a million children had been evacuated. George and Lilian couldn't understand why their children were still at home. They were worried sick until they received their instructions.

And then one day the whole school marched to the station. All the children were in school uniforms. Roger wore his navy blue blazer, grey shorts and socks. Over the top he wore his navy blue mac and his school cap. Round his neck was a cord with his identity disc tied to it so that people would always know who he was. And in a small shoulder bag he carried his gas mask.

The station was packed with children all dressed alike. There were other schools there as well as Roger's. He was pleased to see the uniforms of Gerry's school though he couldn't see Gerry. But Margaret's class was only two down the platform from his so he could see her all right.

A train arrived and they all climbed on. None of the children knew where they were going and as the day wore on the train didn't seem to know either. It travelled slowly and never seemed to stop exactly in a station. It stopped just outside, or moved backwards and forwards, shunting from one line to another. From eleven in the morning to nine o'clock at night it wandered about – and then at last it stopped in a station. A loud railway voice shouted:

"Beddingford. Beddingford Station. All change please."

Hundreds of tired children climbed out of the train onto the platform and the teachers lined them up in their classes. The classes marched out of the station, down a hill, across a long bridge with twenty-four arches – not that anybody counted them that night. Once they were over the river Beddle they climbed the steepest hill Roger had ever climbed in his life.

They came to a large, dark church hall, cold and brown and smelling of dust. They sat on the floor and each of them was given a bun and a cup of tea. The mayor of Beddingford was there with a gold chain around his neck. He made a speech of welcome but Roger was too tired to listen – though he did notice that the mayor spoke with an accent he had never heard before. It sounded very strange and a long way from home.

When the mayor had finished, one of the head teachers made the shortest possible speech of thanks before they got on with the job of sending the children to their evacuation homes. Roger's teacher turned to her class and said:

"Listen for your names. When you hear them you must call out 'Yes sir' in a very loud voice and go to the front. A taxi driver will take you to your new homes. I shall see you at your new school tomorrow and quite soon I shall visit your homes to see how you are getting on."

A man started to call out their names starting with the A's and working through the alphabet. He had the same kind of accent as the mayor. It made their names sound different. Roger watched as

75

one by one his friends went to the front and were taken away. Harry Andrews was one of the first. Soon after that Rex Cook, and then after a while Joan Liddell and Peter Miles. It seemed ages before Jimmy Smith, his friend was called and the hall was almost empty when at last he heard the man call out:

"Wallace. Gerry, Roger and Margaret."

They all shouted "Yes sir" from different parts of the hall and went to the front. Only Iris Williams was left in Roger's class but Miss Smythe went over to keep her company.

Gerry was sent off on his own and then a taxi driver took charge of Roger and Margaret. He had two suitcases with their names on which they hadn't seen since they were on holiday. Their mum must have packed them without their knowing anything about it. The taxi driver was a nice cheerful man.

"Come along you two," he said. "You're lucky. You'm gwain to live together. I'll take you to your new home. I expect you'll be glad to get to bed."

They got into his car and drove through the town. He pointed to a school and said, "That's where you will be going to school. And the house you will live in is right near to it so you won't have far to walk."

With that he turned left into a street of terraced houses and stopped about half way along. As the children stepped out of the car the front door of a house opened. A thin old man stood there. He said to the taxi driver, "These the children then?"

"Yes," answered the driver, "and these are their cases. Where shall I put them?"

The man wheezed. "Take them through to the back room and you children come through as well."

Roger took Margaret's hand and led the way. The front door opened into the front room which looked like a dining-room and a sitting-room all squashed into one. It was crowded with a table and chairs and two armchairs and a small table in one corner with a big box over it.

The children followed the taxi driver through this room to the one behind it. It was almost filled with a large double-bed. The taxi driver put their cases down, wished them well and was gone. The old man grumbled as if it was their fault:

"It's taken you long enough to get here. I'm Mr Small. Mrs Small has gone to bed. That's your bed. If you want a drink there's some water and two glasses by the wash-stand over there. This door," and he walked across to it and opened it, "leads to the kitchen and the backyard. You'll find the lavatory out there. Lock the door when you come in and stay in bed until Mrs Small tells you to get up."

Without another word he shut the door into the kitchen, walked across the room to the door into the front room and went up the stairs. They were very steep and set between the front and back rooms.

Roger and Margaret felt very small and very alone. They were still holding hands. They went out through the tiny little kitchen into the back yard and found the lavatory. Then they came back to the bedroom, had a drink of water and got ready for bed.

"I don't know how to turn the light off," said Roger. "It isn't the same as ours."

"Perhaps you'd better ask," answered Margaret.

Roger stood at the bottom of the stairs and called out, "Excuse me."

There was no answer.

"Excuse me . . . Mr Small."

"Well what is it?" came a harsh voice from the top of the stairs.

"I can't turn the light off."

"Hm," grunted Mr Small. "Never seen a gas light I suppose. Get into bed and I'll come down and see to it."

He came downstairs carrying a candle. Two chains hung down either side of the gas light. He pulled the shorter one and the light fizzled out. Then he grunted "good night" and left the room, shutting the door behind him.

Roger and Margaret cuddled up close to one another in the dark. They felt as if they were Hansel and Gretel lost in the forest and frightened. But they were so tired that they were soon asleep.

# 14

# Hansel and Gretel

They were still fast asleep when Mrs Small called them.

"Wake up you children. Come on, wake up. There's some nice hot water in the bowl for your wash. Breakfast will soon be ready."

She went out into the kitchen and Roger and Margaret got up and washed, using the same water. Roger went to the kitchen and asked:

"Excuse me, Mrs Small, but what do we do with the water we have washed in?"

"Just leave it where it is," she answered. "I'll see to that after you've gone to school."

So they left the bowl of water on the wash-stand and made their bed. Then they just stood in the room together holding hands.

"Do you think we should go into the kitchen?" asked Margaret.

"I don't know," replied Roger. "I think we'd better just stay here until she tells us where to go."

So they just stood.

After a little while Mrs Small came in from the kitchen with two plates of bacon and eggs.

"Why are you just standing there," she asked. "Go into the front room and sit up to the table."

So they went into the front room. Mr Small was sitting, wheezing in an armchair by the empty fireplace. In a cage in the corner there was a parrot. As soon as it saw them it said:

"Pretty Polly. Pretty Polly."

They had never seen a parrot before and they were fascinated by it but Mr Small said, "Shut up."

To their amazement the parrot responded with, "Pretty Polly. Shut up you bugger."

"Shut that bloody parrot up Mother," said Mr Small.

His wife put a cover over the cage which silenced the parrot completely. Roger and Margaret had never heard swearing in their home before and it didn't seem right somehow. It was a bit frightening. They must have shown something of their feelings because Mrs Small said:

"Watch your language Dad. I don't think these kids are used to it." Then she turned to them with some impatience and said, "Sit up to the table then. Don't just stand there."

So they moved to sit down and it was then that they saw the dog. They weren't used to dogs at home and it seemed to them the biggest they had ever seen. It was covered with curly brown fur with black patches and seemed to fill the whole space under the table. They didn't know it but the dog was an Airedale terrier. They felt sure that it must be very fierce and it took all their courage to sit up to the table.

But they were even more scared of Mr and Mrs Small than they were of the dog, so they sat and ate their breakfast in silence. Mrs Small watched them eat.

"If you want a drink there's water in the tap in the kitchen. And when you've finished get ready for school."

So, when they had finished they got themselves a drink and then prepared themselves for school. Mrs Small saw them out of the front door and pointed down the road.

"The school's down there. Off you go and be good kids. And come straight home when school is over."

Margaret grabbed Roger's hand and they walked down the road to school. It was an old, grimy red-brick building similar to their school at home. Some of their friends were already in the playground but no one was playing. It was strangely quiet. They were just standing around in small groups watched by a lot of other children – strangers – and somehow the strangers all seemed bigger than they were even though they were all children of similar ages.

Roger and Margaret joined their friends until the school bell rang. They lined up in their classes in the playground just as they did at home and their teachers came and led them into their class-rooms. They had their own teachers and their own school friends with them but somehow it wasn't the same. They were uncomfortable.

At break they all had their usual drink of milk and they all stayed for school dinners. After dinner they went out into the playground. The Beddingford children were there waiting for them. They divided them up into small groups and herded them into corners. Roger and Margaret found themselves all alone, surrounded by Beddingford children. One of these, a boy aged about eleven, said:

"You come from Lunnon don't ee."

"No," Roger answered.

"Ees ee do."

"No we don't."

"Well where do ee come from then?"

"Near Croydon," answered Roger.

"Where's that then?"

"It's . . . It's . . . " Roger suddenly realised that he didn't know where it was. It wasn't all that far from London but Roger wasn't going to admit that. And it wasn't *all* that far from the sea but he didn't know exactly where it was. So he said, "It's a very long way from here but because of the war we aren't allowed to say exactly where."

"Gyah. 'Tis Lunnon. Us knows 'tis Lunnon and the sooner you go back the better. Us don' want ee."

Roger was a bit scared of this boy but he was angry too and he answered much more bravely than he felt.

"We don't want to be here either – not with you lot. If we could go home we would but we can't. We're evacuees."

"Don't you talk so cocky. Us knows all about you. Us knows you'm 'vacuees. But us don't want ee. This yer's our school and our town, so you just remember."

Roger didn't answer. He thought it was better to stay quiet.

"Answer me when I'm speaking to ee," snapped the boy.

"What am I supposed to say?" asked Roger.

"Don't ee be so cheeky or I'll hit ee one," answered the boy, and some of the other children began to chant:

"Yes George, go on, 'it un one. Go on George. Dap un down."

Roger began to get ready for a fight but just then the bell rang and they all went back into their classes.

After school he found Margaret as quickly as he could and hurried straight back to Mr and Mrs Small's house. They sat in the front room with the dog and the parrot. There was nothing to do. The parrot kept on saying "Pretty Polly" and it wasn't long before they lost interest in it.

As for the dog, they were too scared of that to try to make friends with it. So they just sat and read books until tea was ready. Mrs Small had cooked them egg and chips for tea, and after tea they went straight to bed. They cuddled into one another and talked in whispers for a long time before they went to sleep.

"I hope this war's over soon," thought Roger. "I want to go home."

The next day was very much like the first but the evacuee children kept together more. Jimmy Smith and Roger had got together again but they were very surprised when Harold Brow came up to them and said to Roger, "Roger Wallace, we've got to be friends."

The two had been sworn enemies for nearly a year – ever since they had had a fight over Rachel Pollard. Both still wanted her for their girlfriend whilst she was quite happy to have both of them and lots more boys besides. The business over the Christmas presents had also not been forgotten. It had been a terrific scrap and they had been enemies ever since. So Roger felt quite suspicious.

"Why do you want to be friends?"

"All of us evacuees have got to be friends so that we can fight these Beddingford kids."

"We'd be daft to fight them," answered Roger, "unless they fight us first. There's lots more of them than there is of us."

"Yeah," said Jimmy with a swagger, "but we're better fighters."

"Perhaps," answered Roger, "but we don't know for sure. Anyway Harold's right. It would be best if all of us evacuee kids stick together. OK. We'll be friends."

So they shook little fingers, crossed their hearts and swore, "Friends for life."

That evening when Roger and Margaret got home from school, Mrs Small said, "One of your teachers came here today. She was real nosey – wanted to see everything, even the lav. But she

81

seemed quite a decent sort of girl for all that."

"What was her name?" asked Roger.

"Miss Binns."

"That's my teacher," Margaret said shyly. "I like her."

That ended that conversation and they sat down to their books before another meal of egg and chips and then bed.

The third day was a Friday. It was just the same as Wednesday and Thursday but after school Miss Binns called Margaret and said, "I want you to find your brother please and bring him to see me. I'd like to have a little chat with you both."

So Margaret found Roger and took him to Miss Binns.

"Hello Roger. I went to see your new home yesterday."

"Yes. Mrs Small told us."

"Do you like it there?"

Roger wondered if he ought to tell. He didn't want to be unkind to Mr and Mrs Small. So at first he just fidgeted and said, "It's all right I suppose."

"You mean that you don't like it very much," said Miss Binns. "I thought perhaps you didn't. Mr and Mrs Small are very good people in their way but they have never had any children of their own. They probably don't know how to make you happy."

When Miss Binns said that, Roger and Margaret felt they could tell her all about how they hated it with Mr and Mrs Small. Miss Binns just listened. Most of her children were all right though they didn't like being away from home. But there were several who were frightened and miserable and she had worked very hard to find them decent homes. Because Roger and Margaret had had one another she had left them until last. Now she had plans for them.

"I think I know a house where you would be happy Roger. Would you like to try it?"

"Yes please Miss Binns, I would."

"There's just one snag," Miss Binns added. "Margaret wouldn't be with you."

Margaret grabbed Roger's hand and he started to say, "Oh well that's different . . . "

But Miss Binns interrupted him and turned to Margaret and said, "I thought perhaps you might like to come and live in the same house as me. And you could see Roger very often."

Margaret let go of Roger's hand. Go and live with Miss Binns.

Oh! That would be heaven. She forgot all about Roger.

"Oh yes Miss," she said. "I'd love that."

"Well Roger, what do you say?" asked Miss Binns. "You are the one who will be on your own."

"That's OK. Miss," said Roger. "I expect I'll be all right. Anything will be better than . . . "

He stopped. He didn't want to say too much about Mr and Mrs Small. Miss Binns was probably right – they just didn't understand children.

"Very well then. I'll come home with you and tell Mrs Small and tomorrow morning I'll take you to your new homes."

So it was all arranged. Roger and Margaret had one more dinner and one more breakfast with wheezy Mr Small and Polly and the dog, and one more night in the big double bed, and then their stay in their first evacuation home was over.

# 15

# Barbara

Soon after breakfast that Saturday Miss Binns arrived with Miss Smythe. They took Roger and Margaret with their two suitcases and walked to the end of the road by the school. There they stood and waited for a trolley-bus.

It was the first time they had ever been on a trolley-bus so they were quite excited. They climbed on and went upstairs. It was exactly like any other double-decker bus but over the roof there was a bar which ran underneath an overhead cable so that the bus could be driven by electricity.

As they pulled away from the bus stop there was just a light whirring sound but no real noise even though they were going uphill. Roger had always hated noise. Steam engines at the railway station frightened him with the racket they made. This seemed perfect to him. He loved it.

After about half a mile they all got off the bus and went to the boarding house where Margaret was going to live with the two teachers. It was just like any other seaside boarding house – a bit faded and neglected looking with a notice in the window saying 'No Vacancies.' Margaret had a little room all her own and felt very happy that she was going to live in the same house as Miss Binns and Miss Smythe.

They stayed there all morning and had lunch together and then the teachers took them for a long walk in the park. They played on the swings and roundabouts and went up and down the slide and forgot all about being evacuees. Then the teachers took them home for tea.

After tea they all set off with Roger to take him to his new home. It was only two streets away – a road full of semi-detached houses, all nicely painted in different colours. Roger rang the door-bell and it was opened by a young woman with a nice, friendly freckly face and a tremendous mane of ginger hair. It was swept straight up from her forehead and ran down onto her shoulders in long waves.

"Hello Miss Binns, Miss Smythe. Come in all of you. Come and have a cup of tea."

So they all went in and Roger was introduced to his new landlady, Mrs Bacon. Her husband Tom was a soldier away in France.

She sat them down in the front room and went to make the tea. Like most front rooms in those days it was quite clear that it wasn't used very often. It was kept for best. The fireplace had a tapestry in front of it and there were empty vases and ornaments on the mantelpiece. The three piece suite was new – imitation leather, brown and very cold to Roger with his short trousers and Margaret with her short dress.

There was a piano which looked as if no one ever played it, and that had more empty vases and a couple of photos on it. And in the bay window there was a large brass pot with a huge, ugly plant in it.

But if the room was stiff, Mrs Bacon certainly wasn't. She had her wireless playing in the kitchen and came clattering in with tea for the teachers and lemonade made with lemonade crystals for the children. There were biscuits too and those made Roger feel that he was going to like it with Mrs Bacon. They sat and chatted for a while and then the teachers got up to go.

"Oh, by the way Mrs Bacon," said Miss Binns. "The children didn't have a bath last night so perhaps Roger could have one tonight. And tomorrow we'd like him to be at our house by half past ten so that he can take Margaret to Sunday School. Then he can spend the rest of the day with us."

"OK," Mrs Bacon answered. "I shall have to get up early tomorrow won't I," and she laughed.

Roger was to find that she was always laughing and she made him laugh too. She nearly always seemed to be happy.

Margaret and the teachers left and Mrs Bacon showed Roger to his room. It was small like Margaret's, "But it's next to mine," said Mrs Bacon, "and the other room I keep for guests."

Then they went into the bathroom where there was a big, brass gas geyser like the one at home. Mrs Bacon turned on the hot tap and there was a great roar from the geyser as the gas flared up.

"Do you bath yourself or do you need me to help you?" she asked.

Roger felt a bit shy. At home his mum or dad always came in at bath-time and made sure that he got himself really clean but Mrs Bacon was a stranger; and quite young too.

"I bath myself thank you," he answered.

"Well don't forget behind your ears and the back of your neck and between your toes," she said, and again that bell-like laugh rang out. "If you don't get yourself properly clean I shall have to come in with a scrubber. I want you nice and sparkling for your Miss Binns tomorrow. And make sure you dry yourself properly."

So Roger bathed himself very carefully and swished the water round to wash the bath afterwards, and then went downstairs in his pyjamas, dressing gown and slippers. Mrs Bacon was in the back room sitting beside the coal fire. The wireless was on and she was looking at a magazine.

She looked him over, ruffled his hair and said, "You look all right to me. Shall we have a game of bagatelle?"

The bagatelle board was on the dining-room table with all its circles of nails and holes for the marbles to fall in. There was a small cue to shoot the marbles with. The two of them played and while they played Mrs Bacon asked all sorts of questions about Roger's home and family.

"Do your mum and dad smoke?" she asked after a while.

"I don't think Mum does – well, I'm not sure. I've never seen her. But Dad does. Every Saturday Margaret and me roll his cigarettes for him with those little machines. And he smokes a pipe as well."

"I smoke quite a lot," said Mrs Bacon, lighting the first cigarette Roger had seen her smoke. "Have you ever smoked?"

"No," answered Roger. "I'm much too young."

He paused and then he said, "There was a time this summer when Dad left half a cigar on the mantelpiece when we were on holiday. I smoked that, but I didn't feel very well afterwards."

Mrs Bacon laughed. "No, I don't suppose you did," she said. "Here, have a puff of this one."

So Roger had his first puff of a cigarette. No one knew how harmful smoking was in those days so most people did it.

"Did your mum and dad find out that you had had the cigar?"

"Not really. Dad wondered where it had gone. I think Mum guessed when she saw how queasy I was. But I've never told anyone before."

"Well you don't need to worry. I won't split on you."

At about half past eight Mrs Bacon said, "What's your bed-time?"

At home it was eight o'clock but Roger always liked to stay up if he could so he said nine.

"We'd better have some supper then. And I think I'll have an early night tonight too. So you can come to bed with me and we'll have a nice cuddle before you go to sleep."

So after supper she took Roger to bed with her, kissed him good-night and cuddled him close to her. He felt warm and cosy.

Mrs Bacon," he whispered. "I like it here living with you."

"That's good," she answered, "but let's have no more of this Mrs Bacon stuff. You call me Barbara. Everyone else does."

Barbara. It sounded the most wonderful name he had ever heard. He could call her 'Barbara'. He'd never called a grown up by her first name before. It made him feel important somehow. He snuggled even closer to her and in no time he was fast asleep .

She looked at this little boy lying so peacefully beside her and her eyes filled with tears. It was all wrong these kids being away from their mums and dads and her Tom being away too. She did so want her Tom. She got so terribly hungry for him.

# 16

# First Taste of the Beddle

The next morning Roger collected Margaret and the two of them went to Sunday School. Neither of them liked it.

At home the Sunday School was light. They had their own percussion band and there was plenty of movement and plenty to do. There were special children's hymn books and classes were small and had their own rooms.

Here in Beddingford the children were all in one group in the hall which was dark and smelled of dust. They sang hymns using the old, torn hymn books that were no longer good enough to use in church. There were long readings from the Bible and longer, meandering prayers and a man at the front of the hall gave a boring talk that no one listened to. There was nothing interesting at all.

But the rest of the day was fine. Miss Binns and Miss Smythe were good fun and took them on the bus two or three miles over the hills to the sea. It was too cold for swimming and most of the beach was closed. It was covered with barbed wire and concrete obstacles and there were land mines under the sand. If the Germans did come they would find it hard to land.

Next to the beach there was a long expanse of rocks full of rock pools with anemones, mussels, winkles and lots of other shell-fish. And there were crabs and small fish.

"What are those things?" asked Roger. "They look a bit like shrimps but they are much bigger aren't they."

"Prawns," said Miss Smythe. "They taste lovely cooked in sea water."

"Can I catch some?"

"You haven't got a net."

"I can use my hands."

"Go on then. Have a try if you like."

He got on his knees and cupped his hands. He dipped them deep into the water and moved ever so gently and slowly towards a prawn. He was close enough to be getting excited and then it whizzed backwards. He tried again, stopping off the backwards escape route. It whizzed forwards. He tried again, backwards, forwards, upwards, downwards, it seemed as if those prawns could go in any direction they liked.

"I can see that we shall have to get you a net so that you can catch us some for tea. Talking of tea, who would like some?" asked Miss Smythe.

"Yes please," they both chorused.

"Come on then." The teachers took them to a beach café.

"That's much better than the beach at Bognor," Roger said.

"I like the sand at Bognor," murmured Margaret.

"Well there's lots of sand here but it's full of land mines so you can't go on it. I expect it's the same at Bognor now. They will have filled that with land mines and barbed wire and things."

They caught the bus back to Beddingford. Most Sundays followed that pattern except that the children stopped going to Sunday school and went to church with the teachers instead. It was just as boring but they felt more grown up and they liked having decent hymn books to sing from.

Weekdays were mostly taken up with school. Roger didn't like it much. It was the evenings and Saturdays that he enjoyed most. Barbara was so easy to get on with. They always had the wireless on and they played all sorts of games together: bagatelle of course, ludo, snakes and ladders, tiddlywinks and lots of different card games.

On his first free Saturday Barbara let Roger go out on his own. As he walked down the front path she shouted after him, "Don't go too near the river. It's dangerous."

Roger wandered down through the town and it wasn't long before he was by the river. He strolled along looking at the small cargo boats from Hull and Liverpool and Bristol. And there were one or two from London that made him think of home, and suddenly he felt a bit homesick.

As he was passing a small, grimy coal boat he saw a boy fishing. The boy was smaller than Roger and was using a hand reel. As Roger watched he put his reel on the ground, pulled in his line and put a new worm on the hook. Then he stood up and threw the hook back into the river. But as he threw it he also kicked his reel. That fell into the river too and began to float down river on the tide.

Roger ran along the river bank and grabbed a hawser which reached from the ship to a bollard on the river-front. He leaned out over the river to save the reel. He caught hold of the reel all right but his weight made the hawser sag down and down. Slowly Roger went with it. He couldn't pull himself back. Eventually he lost his balance and toppled forward, falling into the river with a great splash.

He couldn't swim but he clung onto the hawser. It went down and then slowly began to rise again. It lifted just far enough to carry his head above water and then it started to go down again. Under he went. Up he came again, coughing and spluttering. Down he went again.

The little boy was screaming for help. A seaman ran up, gripped Roger by the arm and hauled him onto the land. Roger gasped and spluttered a bit but he wasn't in serious difficulties. The seaman gave him a mighty whack on the backside and said, "Run off home and get out of those wet clothes, and don't ever trust a ship's rope again."

People stared as Roger ran up the High Street. He came to the back door and knocked hard. Barbara came to the door and roared with laughter when she saw him. Then she said, "You get undressed right there while I run a bath for you. Then when you are nice and warm you can tell me all about it."

She didn't tick him off. But she started taking him to the local swimming pool on learners' nights and made sure that he learned to swim. She used to take him out with her quite a lot.

Sometimes they went to the cinema – to romantic films that didn't really interest him. Sometimes they went to the amusement arcade. That was Barbara's favourite and Roger quite liked it too. She got very excited when she won any money but it wasn't long before she had spent anything she had won. But she always shared her winnings with Roger so that he could have a go on the machines. He liked the ones with cranes that tried to grab presents though they never actually managed to grab hold of anything properly and he never won.

When they were tired of the machines Barbara would grab Roger's hand.

"Come on. Let's go on the ghost train and through the tunnel of love."

She screamed as skeletons lit up before them and again as spiders' webs brushed their faces. She clung to Roger as if she was really scared. And in the tunnel of love she always wanted a cuddle and a kiss. She was nice and soft to cuddle and there was something about her kisses that was different from any kisses he had ever had. She kissed him full on the lips and he found that he liked that.

Sometimes they met soldiers down there.

"Poor chaps. I'll bet they're lonely," said Barbara. "Come on, let's make friends with them."

Before long Roger would find himself with money from a soldier.

"You go and have a go on the bumper cars while I take Mrs here on the ghost train."

Roger learned to keep out of the way until the soldiers brought Barbara back to him. They always seemed very flushed and cheerful. They all walked home together, buying fish and chips on the way. Quite often the soldiers seemed to be free to stay the night but Roger could never quite make out where they slept.

Barbara made a great thing of showing them to the guest room but an awful lot of night noises seemed to come from her bedroom. Roger sometimes felt a bit pushed out of things. But some of the soldiers played cards or bagatelle with him. And they told him lots of stories.

Roger wished that Barbara's husband Tom could come home from France to tell them about the fighting, although there didn't seem to be much fighting going on at the time. Everything was in a kind of limbo. When the troops marched through Beddingford or drilled on the riverside Roger marched up and down alongside them. If there were no officers around the sergeant would sometimes include him:

"Now then youngster. Look lively. Pick 'em up. Pick 'em up. 'eft, righ', 'eft, righ', that's the way of it; HAY BOUT TARN; at the double . . . " and so it would go on.

Christmas came and quite a lot of the evacuees went home. There hadn't been any bombing so they might as well. But George and Lilian came to Beddingford and they all had a queer, cold sort of Christmas in a hotel on the riverside.

Roger and Margaret studied the other guests carefully. Some of them actually *lived* in the hotel. There was one strange little old lady. She always wore her hat, even at meal-times and she didn't like children. It wasn't long before Roger had decided that he knew why.

"English people don't wear hats at meal times," he said to Margaret. "She must be a German. I'll bet she's a spy."

He took to following her about. Sometimes she was aware of it and became quite jumpy and ratty. She had an attic room with its own staircase. One day she found Roger on the stairs.

"What are you doing on my staircase little boy? Go away and stop following me around or I shall tell your parents and have you thrashed."

Roger tried to be more careful but it was difficult with only that flight of stairs to her room. But he did sometimes creep up there when she was inside. He could hear her tap, tap, tapping.

"She must be a spy," Roger explained to Margaret. "That's why she's in the attic, so's she can get her messages out. I can hear her tapping things in code."

"D'you think we ought to tell someone?" asked Margaret.

"No. No one would listen to us. We've got to catch her red-handed."

In the new year, when it was time for the Christmas decorations to come down, she was very insistent that they must all come down.

"It's very unlucky to leave decorations up after twelfth night," she said. "Please make quite sure nothing is left."

"I don't think she's a spy," said Margaret. "I think she's a witch."

"Nah," said Roger. "She's a spy and a fusspot. She's a . . . she's an old fuzzypeg, that's what she is. We'll call her that: 'Fuzzypeg'."

"Yes that's a good name but she's not a spy. She's a witch."

"She's a spy."

"A witch."

Roger went for her but she dodged and ran out of the room and

92

up to her parents' room.

"Roger's going to hit me."

"No I'm not. I'm just chasing that's all."

"He said Fuzzypeg is a spy. But she's not. She's a witch."

"She's a spy."

"Now then," said Lilian. "That's quite enough. We've no spies or witches in this hotel. But who is Fuzzypeg?"

"The lady with the hat," said Margaret.

George started to laugh but Lilian silenced him with a look.

"I don't think that's a very nice name," she said. "She's just a harmless, lonely little lady. Now, why don't you go and offer to help take the decorations down."

Roger was not convinced. He grumbled at Margaret: "You shouldn't have told Mum about Fuzzypeg. If we are not careful she will be on her guard and it will be all the harder to catch her."

They went to the manager and asked if they could help with the decorations. When they had finished, Roger crept up to Fuzzypeg's room and pinned some of the decorations to her bedroom door.

"There. That'll give her some of that bad luck she was talking about. Serves her right for being such a Fuzzypeg."

With the holidays over Mr and Mrs Wallace went back home and the children went back to their evacuation homes ready for the new term at school.

# 17

# The Cloakroom Episode

Out of school the Beddingford children and the evacuees were beginning to mix a bit. But in school they still had most of their classes separately. Because the school was so crowded, break times were spread about all through the day. When one class was using a class room another class would have free time. Often they had to spend it outside even if the weather was bad.

One wet day during Mr Hollingsworth's arithmetic class, Roger was looking out of the window watching the rain come down. He whispered to Jimmy Smith, who was sitting beside him:

"It won't be much fun out there next lesson."

"No," answered Jimmy. "It's only old Westaway's art class. I don't s'pose he'd notice if we stayed here with the Beddingford lot."

That gave Roger an idea. "He certainly wouldn't notice if we stayed here *instead of* the Beddingford lot would he?"

"Of course not but who's going to persuade them to stay out in the rain?" said Jimmy.

"I am," answered Roger. "Well, not in the rain exactly. But I'm going to tell them I've got a message from old Westaway and he wants to see them in the cloakrooms."

"What good will that do?" asked Jimmy.

Roger fished about in his pocket and pulled out a key. "It's the cloakroom key," he said. "I found it a few days ago. I'll lock the Beddingford lot in the cloaks. While I'm doing it, you must tell our lot that the time-table's been changed and that we've got to stay here for Westaway's art class. Don't tell them it's a jape. Just get them to stay."

"OK," answered Jimmy. "Cor. What a super stunt."

Roger put his hand up and asked if he could go to the toilet. Then he went out to where the Beddingford children were huddled up chatting and trying to keep out of the rain.

"Hey you lot," called Roger. "Mr Westaway has sent me. When the bell goes he wants to see all of you in the cloakrooms. He's in a rotten mood. What have you been up to?"

None of them knew what they had been up to but when the bell rang they all hurried off to the cloakrooms wondering what they were in for. Roger followed at a distance. When they were all inside he quietly closed the door and locked it. Then he rushed back to the classroom. Mr Westaway was just beginning his class. Roger apologised for being late.

"I've just been to the toilet sir."

"All right boy. Sit down and let's get on."

For a while everything passed off normally. But the Beddingford children were getting more and more noisy as they waited and waited. Then one of them decided to go and find Mr Westaway and of course, he found that the door was looked. He shouted to the rest to shut up and told them that the door was locked. That started a whole series of arguments about what they should do and the noise grew louder and louder. Eventually they managed to open one of the small top windows and little Mike Roney climbed out . . . right into the arms of the Headmaster who had come to find out what all the noise was about. He unlocked the cloakroom door and stepped inside.

Silence fell.

Holding Mike Roney by the ear he said, "What were you doing climbing through the window?"

"Please sir, trying to get out sir."

"Well you do surprise me," answered the Headmaster sarcastically, "but what were you doing in here in the first place."

"Waiting for Mr Westaway sir."

"I see. Did Mr Westaway tell you to wait here?"

"Yes sir. Well sir. Not zactly sir."

"What do you mean, 'Not exactly'?"

"Well sir. One of they Lunnon children told us us must wait yer."

"Which London child?"

Mike Roney didn't want to get Roger into trouble so he lied, "I don't know his name sir."

"Does anybody know the name of this London child?" asked the headmaster.

Betsy James' hand went up but Mike glared at her and someone else dug her in the ribs, so when the headmaster asked her to speak she stuttered and then said, "No sir. None of us don't know his name."

"I see," said the headmaster. "You are all lying of course. However, in an orderly and quiet fashion go to your classroom."

They hurried off to class three and knocked on the door.

"Come in," called Mr Westaway and looked in astonishment as thirty children filed into the classroom followed by the headmaster.

"Do you mind if I have a word with these two classes Mr Westaway?"

"Of course not sir."

So the head turned to the children and ordered them to sit down. They squeezed together until they were all sitting after a fashion. Then the head asked, "Does anyone here have a key to the cloakrooms?"

Roger stood. He was looking rather pale.

"And what is your name boy?"

"Wallace sir."

"What are you doing with a cloakroom key?"

"I found it sir."

"You found it."

"Yes sir."

"But you didn't hand it in."

"No sir."

"Did you lock Beddingford Class Three in the cloakrooms Wallace?"

"Yes sir."

"And was it your idea to send a message to Beddingford Class Three that Mr Westaway wanted to meet them there?"

"Yes sir."

"Did the rest of your class support you in this Wallace?"

"No sir. I told them there was a change in the timetable and that they had got to stay here. There wasn't anybody else sir."

"Please sir," Jimmy Smith interrupted and jumped up.

"Yes, what is it?" asked the headmaster.

"Please sir, it wasn't Wallace on his own sir. I helped sir."

"I see." He paused for a while and then he said, "this is a very serious business. I shall inform Miss Danbury your headmistress, that I will not have her evacuees disrupting the life of my school. It is bad enough having you here at all. But before I speak to Miss Danbury I'm going to make an example of you two so that nothing of this kind ever happens again. Short of expulsion, the maximum punishment in this school is six of the best. Wallace. And you boy. Come out here."

The boys made their way to the front of the classroom.

"Please sir," said Roger, "Smith wasn't really . . . "

"Oh yes I was," interrupted Jimmy.

"Silence," roared the headmaster. "Mr Westaway kindly fetch me your cane and move the blackboard to the centre of the classroom."

Mr Westaway had never used his cane. He did as the headmaster asked and said as quietly as he could, "Sir. Shouldn't we speak to Miss Danbury *before* punishing the boys?"

"I shall do what I think is right in my own school," answered the head. "Besides, Miss Danbury is going back to her home soon and the schools will be merged under my leadership." Then he said to the boys, "You two boys bend over with your bottoms facing the class, one of you on either side of the blackboard. I shall cane Smith first. You, Wallace, will listen to his cries and know what to expect."

Mr Westaway felt that this was too much. "Sir," he said . . .

But the headmaster stopped him before he could get any further.

"I know what you have in mind Mr Westaway. Kindly take the girls from the classroom. They can wait outside the staff room in silence until the next lesson and you can go straight to your next class."

That was not what Mr Westaway had in mind. He had wanted to ease the boy's punishment and to make it more private. But he did as he was told and left the headmaster alone with the boys.

Roger and Jimmy had been bent over all this time and only wanted to get it over with. The head took the cane and flexed it. Then he brought it down for the first time on Jimmy's bottom. Jimmy gasped and the tears filled his eyes but he gritted his teeth

97

e

and didn't cry out. The second and the third strokes came.

"So, you're playing that silly 'I'll be brave' game are you?" the head murmured very quietly. "Well, you've three to go."

The fourth and fifth strokes fell and finally the last, but Jimmy never made a sound.

"Go to your desk and sit down," ordered the headmaster angrily.

Jimmy walked uncomfortably to his desk and didn't quite sit down.

"Sit down properly," said the headmaster. "That's better. Now Wallace. It's your turn."

All this time Roger had been bending over. He was very frightened, but Jimmy had managed not to cry. He was determined to be as brave as his pal.

The head laid on those six strokes of the cane as hard as he could but Roger never cried out. Like Jimmy, he was ordered to his place and made to sit properly. Then the head spoke to the whole class:

"You will all remain here in silence until the bell goes."

He stalked out of the classroom.

After a while the bell rang and the children went to their next classes. Roger and Jimmy were surprised to see Mr Westaway talking to Miss Binns, who was taking their next class. She nodded to him and called the two boys out. Quietly she said, "I want you two to go to the lavatory before the class begins. Be as quick as you can. We are going to do some acting this class so you will both have standing up parts."

After school Roger and Jimmy found that everyone seemed to know what had happened and the children of both schools seemed to think they were heroes. Quite a crowd walked home with them. Before they separated Roger said to Jimmy:

"You didn't have to get caned. Thanks for sticking with me."

Jimmy held out his little finger. They shook fingers, crossed their hearts and said, "Cross my heart and hope to die."

It was like Indians being blood brothers. They were friends for life.

# 18

# Revenge is Sweet

Quite a crowd of children went to and from school together now. The boys used to play football down the streets or marbles in the gutters. The girls ran hoops, skipped with skipping ropes, or stopped on the way home for a game of hop-scotch. But when winter came it stopped all these games for a while.

It was a very cold winter that winter of 1940 and a lot of snow fell in Beddingford. It wasn't so bad for people like Roger who were well dressed in warm clothes. But quite a lot of the children at his school had old patched clothes that didn't really fit. Some of them had holes in their jackets or shorts. Some had boots but no socks. And a few that had gone bare-foot in the warmer months had their feet wrapped in all sorts of things: rags, bandages, newspapers all done up with string. Roger had never noticed how badly some of them were dressed until now.

He dug a pathway from Barbara's front door to the front gate and across the pavement and he and Barbara made a snowman that lasted for ages.

On the way to and from school snow-fights and slides took the place of all the usual games. The boys enjoyed catching the girls and putting snowballs down their blouses and making them scream. There was a specially good slide that ran across the play-ground at school but snow fights were forbidden.

In spite of that, in the lunch-hour some of the boys went out of the school grounds and way-laid the children who went home for lunch. Roger and Jimmy were first-sitting for lunch so they ate at twelve. From twelve thirty to one was second-sitting and that was free time for Roger and Jimmy.

One lunch-time they were just coming through the school gates to go out to play when they saw the second-sitting eating their lunch. The Headmaster of Beddingford was at the top table. As the sun was shining he had opened the window beside him. He was a bit of a fresh air fanatic. Roger turned to Jimmy and said:

"Wouldn't it be super to throw a snowball through there right into his dinner?"

"Yeah," answered Jimmy, "but it's too far away."

"It is from here but not from that corner of the wall."

"It would have to be a darned good shot."

"Yes, and if you missed the first time you wouldn't get another chance."

"Anyway he'd see you and you'd get another six whacks."

"He might. But not if you ducked down quick behind the wall and got away."

"All right," said Jimmy, "I'll stand by the school gate and watch. Then I can tell you what happens."

But Roger was beginning to get the wind up. "I didn't say I was going to do it. I only said it would be super if someone did."

"Well why don't you do it then?"

"Suppose he did see me."

"He won't see," said Jimmy.

"He will you know. He sees everything."

"You're yeller," said Jimmy.

"No I'm not."

"Well do it then."

"I dunno," answered Roger.

"Go on. I *dare* you."

That did it. Any doubts Roger might have had were wiped away. A dare was a challenge he had to accept. He had another look at the spot he had chosen to throw from. There were some large trees beside the school. One of them was right by the boundary wall. If he threw from there he might get away unseen.

He made himself a good, firm snowball, took three quick steps and hurled it as hard as he could. Then he darted behind the tree and peeped.

"Bull's-eye," yelled Jimmy from his hiding place.

The snowball had hit the headmaster full in the face. Roger didn't waste a moment. He dashed along the boundary wall and ignored the shout of "Come here that boy!" which the headmaster directed in the hope that he would frighten the culprit into the open. Roger ran on and raced into school through the side gate. Once inside he was able to join the children who were in the playground and mingle with them as if he had never been outside.

Jimmy had also been very careful to keep out of sight. He came into the playground from the other side and joined Roger.

"You did it," he grinned with glee. "Got 'im right in the kisser. Brilliant."

"Sh," said Roger. "Behave as if nothing has happened and we have been here all through dinner."

But Jimmy was too excited. Soon all the children knew what had happened. Roger was a hero all over again.

He enjoyed telling Barbara all about it when he got home that evening. She laughed and laughed.

They had their usual meal together and played their usual games. Then they went to bed in Barbara's bed and sat up smoking cigarettes and talking. Barbara asked, "Have you noticed anything different about me lately?"

Roger looked at her face and studied it carefully. "No," he answered.

"Haven't you noticed how fat I'm getting?"

Roger looked down at her tummy. He hadn't noticed but now he looked at it he could *see*. It was quite big.

"Oh that," he said. "Yes I'd noticed that."

"You never said anything," said Barbara.

"Well it would have been rude wouldn't it."

"I don't think you even noticed."

"Course I did," said Roger.

"Well," explained Barbara, "I'm fat because I'm going to have a baby. Here. Put your hand on my tummy and you can feel it moving."

As Roger looked he could see the movements but he put his hand on her tummy just the same. He certainly could feel the baby. Barbara carried on explaining:

"Before Tom went to France we decided not to wait until the war is over before having a baby. Otherwise we might have to wait a long time. So I'm going to have one quite soon."

She paused but Roger didn't say anything so she went on.

"The trouble is I shall need your room for the baby."

"That's OK," answered Roger cheerfully. "I can go in the guest room."

"No. You don't understand." Barbara was looking very embarrassed and uncomfortable. "I've got to keep the guest room for the soldiers. You are going to have to move to a different house."

Roger looked at her in horror. Then he almost shouted, "Why should I have to go? You don't HAVE to have soldiers here. I don't want to go."

"Things are changing," answered Barbara sadly. "So far we've had soldiers here because I wanted to be kind to them. But now the army has told me that I've got to have some billeted here all the time. So you see, you've got to go."

"It's not fair. Why should they pick on me? I want to stay here."

Barbara began to cry. "I don't want you to go either," she said. "I love you too much. But I haven't got any say in it."

Roger was hurt and angry. And he had a queer feeling that she wasn't exactly telling him the truth. He jumped out of her bed and ran into his own room. There he let his feelings go. He cried and cried until he had cried himself to sleep.

A little while later Barbara crept into his room. She saw that he had been crying and that started her crying all over again. Carefully she tucked his bedclothes in and then she knelt beside the bed and kissed him and stroked his hair. She was so gentle that he didn't wake up so he didn't hear her as she told him the truth.

"I really don't want you to go Roger my love. But people have been saying bad things about me because of the soldiers I bring home. They have reported me to the school and the school people say I can't keep you any more. Oh Roger. I'm ever so sorry. I do love you you know."

She cried some more and then she dragged herself to her feet and wiped the tears away. "I do hope they find somewhere nice for you where you'll be happy," she whispered as she crept out of his room and back to her own bed.

# 19

# Murder

But Roger was not the only one moving on.

One morning they were at school and Jimmy wanted to go to the lavatory. Up went his hand and Mr Westaway let him go. The lavatories were outside in a corner of the playground so it was always a good escape from the classroom to go.

No sooner had he gone than a short, plump, cheerful little lady tapped on the classroom door and came in.

All the children stood up politely.

Mr Westaway told them to sit and then he and the lady had a chat. She was one of the school's Voluntary Helpers. Her job was to keep an eye on the homes of the evacuees to see that they were as happy as they could be.

After she had spoken to Mr Westaway he looked up and said, "Jimmy Smith, come forward please."

Roger put his hand up and said, "Please sir. You said he could go to the lav, sir."

"Oh yes. So I did. Well Wallace, please go and tell him to hurry up because Mrs Pusey has come to see him."

Off went Roger and it wasn't long before he was back.

"Please sir. Jimmy says there isn't any paper in the lavs and I've looked and there isn't any in any of them."

"Oh dear. We must see to that," said Mr Westaway. He tore a few sheets out of an exercise book and gave them to Roger and said, "Please tell Jimmy to hurry. Mrs Pusey hasn't got all day."

Roger set off at a run but within a moment or two he appeared in the doorway again, this time with Jimmy who was grinning all over his face.

"It's all right sir. I didn't need the paper after all. I found a bus ticket sir."

The whole class started giggling. Mr Westaway shut them up and sent Jimmy to wash his hands. When that was done, he and Mrs Pusey went outside for a talk.

It turned out that he had got to move house too. He was going to live in the part of Beddingford which was the other side of the river, near the old fort. Local people called it Eastriver and the main town they called Westriver.

So a few days later they both moved – to opposite ends of the town. Roger moved to a dark little back street terraced house, the home of Mr and Mrs Blount.

There were two bedrooms upstairs and two rooms downstairs, a living room and a kitchen with a cold water tap. The toilet was out in the yard and the house was lit by gas. It was a bit like the first house where Roger and Margaret had been billeted, only it was a bit dingy and dark and it wasn't as big.

Mrs Blount seemed pleasant enough but Mr Blount hardly said a word. He was thin, smoked endless cigarettes and coughed a lot. After a bad coughing bout he would spit into the fire. They had a dog, a mongrel that stayed so close to Mr Blount that you would almost have thought they were joined together.

Roger arrived at mid-day in time for dinner and afterwards they let him go out on his own as usual. He went to the cattle market and met Jimmy Smith there. Jimmy seemed quite pleased with his new home. He and Roger often came to the cattle market.

They were both fascinated by it. They had never seen anything like it and neither of them knew much about farming. So on a Saturday they would watch the sheep, cattle and pigs being bought and sold and on Tuesdays they went up to the slaughter-house and watched animals being killed.

The animals were led into a large, tiled, open room. A gun was placed on the side of their head and fired. They died at once. Then a knife slashed their throats to let the blood run out into bowls and they were taken away to be skinned and cut up. The boys particularly liked watching the sheep being skinned.

The sheep and the cattle were usually calm and quiet and died without any fuss, but the pigs seemed to know what lay ahead.

They kicked up a terrible racket, squealing and fighting all the way.

But today was Saturday so it was just a day for buying and selling. The auctioneer stood at a desk out in the open shouting out, "What am I bid for this fine flock of sheep?"

And all the farmers stood around watching to see what price they would fetch. The auctioneer called out the bids until it was clear that he was going to get no more. Then he wrapped up the bidding with:

"Going to the man in the pork pie hat – thank you sir. Going for the first time. Going, going," (a slight pause and then with a rush) "gone to the man with the pork pie hat." And with each 'going' he hammered on his desk with a wooden hammer, finishing with a great flourish on 'gone'.

At tea-time the two boys went their separate ways home. Roger went in for his tea and after tea Mr Blount prepared to shave. He took his cut-throat razor and ran it up and down a leather strop which was hanging on the kitchen door. When the blade was to his liking he took the kettle off the fire and filled his shaving mug. He wet his face and rubbed his shaving stick soap over his stubble. Then he took his shaving brush and worked the soap up into a good lather. The razor rasped against his face as he cut the stubble off. Then he rinsed off with cold water, put on a scarf and jacket and turned to Roger and said:

"Come on boy. Us mus' take th'ol dog for his walk."

It was the same routine every day, and the same walk. First they walked down to the river, then along the water-front and into the King Edward park. They walked right round the inside of the park, back along the water-front and up the hill back to their house. Mr Blount never spoke to Roger on these walks. Occasionally he spoke to the dog and every fifty yards or so he made a loud gargling noise and spat horrible yellow stuff into the river or on the flower beds in the park.

Roger hated his spitting and because of it he hated these walks. Soon he hated Mr Blount:

That first night, when they got back from their walk Mrs Blount offered Roger some cocoa. Then she took him up to his bedroom. It had a large double bed in it and very little space for anything else.

"This is your new bedroom my dear," said Mrs Blount. "Us

didn't say nothing to the school lady but Mr Blount and me don't sleep in the same room any more. So us have put you in with he."

Roger was horrified but she didn't seem to notice. She just chattered on.

"Us have fixed a big plank down the middle of the bed so you won't get mixed up. You sleep this side near the door in case you want to go to the toilet in the night. Mr Blount will sleep on the t'other side. There. I think that explains everything. Good night my dear. Sleep well."

And with that she left Roger on his own. He shuddered. Fancy having to go to bed with that horrible man. He thought of Barbara, all soft and warm and cuddly. Why couldn't he have stayed with her? He hated it here.

He got into bed and fortunately he fell asleep almost at once.

They washed in the kitchen so that's where Roger washed next morning, in cold water. As it was Sunday he spent his usual day with Margaret and the teachers. They said:

"We won't ask you how you like your new home until you've had a bit longer to get used to it."

So he didn't have the chance to tell them that he didn't like it at all.

The new week passed by: school by day, tea, and then the dreaded walk and the nights in the shared bed. Sometimes Roger was still awake when Mr Blount came wheezing and coughing up the stairs. Then he was frightened as well as miserable.

One Friday night Roger lay there rigid while Mr Blount got into bed. Quite soon he was snoring away loudly and not long afterwards Roger himself went to sleep.

In the middle of the night, still fast asleep, Roger got out of bed. He walked right round the bed and climbed on top of Mr Blount. Then he put his hands round Mr Blount's scraggy neck and said, "I hate you. I'm going to murder you."

He squeezed as hard as he could and then he crawled to the bottom of the bed and sat on the end of the bed facing the window. Mr Blount wasn't hurt but strangely enough he was scared.

After a little while Roger came back and did the same thing again, saying the same words – and Mr Blount didn't move.

Roger returned to the bottom of the bed and sat there for a while. Then he came back a third time and again he said, "I hate you. I'm going to murder you."

And for the third time he tried to strangle Mr Blount while Mr Blount lay quite still. Then Roger got off the bed, walked round it to his own side and laid down and slept as if nothing had happened.

Mr Blount was shaking from head to foot. He got up and put his clothes on and went downstairs. He got himself a large neat gin, built up the fire and sat down beside it. Slowly his fear turned to anger and a sense of frustration. He ought to have given that boy a good hiding, that's what.

Because he was so angry he hardly slept a wink but he was sleeping when Mrs Blount came down in the morning and quite crotchety when she woke him up asking him what he was doing sitting there beside the fire. He told her what had happened and she was horrified.

"Oh my. Oh my dear soul. How could he say such things. Oh my. An' did ee really try to strangle ee. Oh my. 'Tis terrible in' it. Oh dearie me. Ee'll 'ave to go. Yes. This very day. Us can't have that. Such goings on. Oh my."

On and on she went until Roger came downstairs. Mr Blount rounded on him angrily.

"You tried to murder me last night."

Roger was amazed. "What," he said.

He thought Mr Blount was joking until he looked at the man. Mr Blount told him exactly what had happened but Roger found it hard to take it in, let alone to believe it. He had no recollection of these things at all. Could it be true. As far as he knew he had never been sleep-walking before. But Mr Blount was so wound up and went on about it so much that he felt he had to believe him.

And when Mrs Blount joined in and told him he was an ungrateful wretch and that he would have to move on that very day he realised that it really was true.

They kept on and on and Roger began to feel trapped. His head began to feel as if it would burst. Suddenly he jumped up from his chair, grabbed his coat and ran out of the house. He ran down to the river and then turned away from the park and ran up river.

He was soon out of the town. He left the road and as he followed the riverside footpath he stopped running. Steep wooded hills rose on both sides of the river. The morning sun shone down on the water and Roger saw a cormorant fishing. He sat down by the water's edge and watched.

The cormorant disappeared under water. Roger tried to guess where it would surface – but he was wrong by a long way. He watched again, guessed again, was wrong again. He tried counting the seconds while the cormorant was under water: "One-and, two-and, three-and . . . " the way his brother had taught him to count seconds. And he tried holding his breath to see if he could last as long as the cormorant did – but he couldn't. Every so often it came up with a fish, wriggled it around in its beak and then swallowed it.

At last it flew low across the water to a large rock that jutted out from the bank. There it stood and held out its wings to dry. Roger watched for a long time. Then he started skimming stones across the water to see how many times they would bounce before they sank.

Then he walked on up the river generally messing about and enjoying himself and forgetting all about everyone. But as the day wore on he began to get hungry. And that made him wonder what the time was.

"Oh gosh," he thought, "I'm in enough trouble already. I'd better not be late for dinner."

And then he stopped.

"Blow dinner," he said out aloud. "I'm not going back there. I'm not. I'm not. I'm not. Never."

He felt better after that. But what was he going to do? Perhaps he should run away? Where to?

If he went back and over the river he could find Jimmy Smith. Together they could find some place where he could hide and Jimmy could bring some food to him. Yes, that was the best idea. So he set off down river towards the bridge. Back along the footpath he went, out onto the road and it was there that he bumped into Barbara.

"Hello," she said cheerfully, "what are you doing?"

He didn't answer. He just burst into tears and ran into her arms.

She cuddled him close the way she always did and made him feel warm and safe. Then she said, "You'd better come home with me and have some chips. Come on."

So she took him home and cooked him sausages and eggs and chips and while he was eating he told her all about the Blounts and what had happened the night before. When he got to that bit she laughed so merrily that he felt better about it and began to giggle a bit himself.

"Don't you worry," said Barbara. "We'll talk to your Miss Binns and she won't let you go back there."

"I wish I could come back here," said Roger.

"Yes dear so do I, but I don't think they'll let you stay here either. Never mind. You're here now. I tell you what. You're a bit dirty so you go up and have a nice bath and then we'll go and tell Miss Binns where you are."

So she turned on the old geyser that roared and shook and gave out its usual hot water and Roger had a good bath. When he came down he and Barbara had a long cuddle and then went to see Miss Binns.

She had already heard the story from Mr and Mrs Blount but, after she had got Barbara a cup of tea she asked Roger to tell her all about his life at the Blount's house. When he had finished she said:

"I think perhaps you had better stay with us and Margaret for the weekend while we decide what's to be done with you. We can't have you going round trying to murder people can we. And you don't need to go back to Mr and Mrs Blount. I'll go round there and tell them that you won't be back and I'll bring all your things back here when I come."

Then she called Margaret and Roger went off with his sister. Barbara said, "I could have him back with me you know."

"Yes I know," said Miss Binns, "and I wish I could allow it. But you know why I can't."

"Because of gossip," Barbara answered bitterly – and then she went on sadly, "well it's not just gossip I suppose. A lot of it's true. But I get lonely without Tom. You understand."

"Yes I understand and I'm not sure we are right to take Roger away from you. I doubt if he'll find anywhere where he'll be as happy as he was with you. But one thing you can be sure of. We shan't put him with any more people like the Blounts."

So Barbara went home and Roger spent the weekend with his sister. Although they were developing different interests and living separate lives they were still good friends – well most of the time – and it was nice to be together again.

When Monday came, he and Margaret went to school together and by the evening a new home had been found for him – over the river near to Jimmy Smith.

# 20

# Eastriver

So after tea Miss Binns took Roger to his new home. They took the bus across the river, round by the station and up the hill. Then they walked through to Fort Park. Roger had never seen this side of Beddingford before, except from a distance. But when he saw the fort high on the hill at the top of the park, he felt that it would be a good place to explore.

They walked up the road beside the park to a small house with a tiny front garden. The door brasses were brightly polished and the door step scrubbed clean. Mrs Guthrie opened the door to them. She was a short, tubby woman with a round, friendly face and grey hair done up in a bun at the back of her head.

She took them inside and showed them all over the house – even her own bedroom. Roger had a small, light bedroom over-looking the park. It looked very cosy and spotlessly clean. At the back of the house was a small, neat garden and beyond the back gate there was a patch of waste ground.

Mr Guthrie was sitting by the coal-fire in the living room, puffing a pipe and reading. He was also small and tubby, with short grey hair and a brown, crinkly face and twinkling eyes.

Mrs Guthrie made a pot of tea and brought it in with a plate of home made rock cakes. Roger hadn't tasted such nice cakes since he had been at home before the war. He felt sure that he was going to be happy with Mr and Mrs Guthrie – and he was right.

It was that first evening after Miss Binns had gone that Mrs Guthrie said, "I'm sorry you didn't like Mr Blount dear. But I'm not altogether surprised. Now. Just think for a moment. Can you think of something nice to tell me about him?"

It was an unexpected question and Roger did have to think before he found an answer.

"Yes," he said. "There is one thing. He was very fond of that dog of his and the dog was very fond of him."

"There dear. Always remember that it doesn't matter who it is, you can always find something nice to say about people if you try. There is something good in everybody. All you've got to do is to look for it.

Take those Blounts for example. They're a strange lot but I wouldn't like you to think that they are bad people. You saw yourself how Mr Blount loved his dog. And it was just the same with his father when he was alive.

"His father was the captain of a little old coaster that used to run out of Beddingford harbour to Bristol and Liverpool and across to Ireland sometimes. Everyone used to call him 'Skipper'.

"All his time as captain he used to have a dog on board and he loved those dogs more than anyone – more than his wife and more than his son. And because people called him 'Skipper' he called his dogs 'Skip'.

"Eventually he retired to their tiny little cottage down where you were and soon afterwards his wife died. But he didn't mind. He was perfectly happy living there on his own with his pipe and his old dog Skip.

"They were inseparable. He never needed a lead. The dog almost seemed to be attached to him. Indoors and outdoors the two of them were always together and Skip never wandered far from his master's side. It was wonderful to see them.

"In the end Skipper died quietly of old age in his armchair by the fire. It was Skip who alerted people because he just sat by Skipper's side and howled and howled until they came.

"Skip didn't interfere when they came to lay the old man out nor when they took him to the church for the funeral. He just sat close to and watched.

"The undertaker was an old friend and he took Skip in the hearse to the church but the vicar wouldn't let him take the dog inside.

"However, when they started the procession with the vicar leading the way, Skip slipped underneath the coffin and went in with it. But he seemed to understand that he mustn't let the vicar

111

see him because he slipped into the shadows out of sight until the service was over and then followed them all to the grave.

"After the burial he disappeared – but not for long. When everyone had gone away he came back to the grave and sat there. The sexton and the vicar tried to shoo him away but he would only slink away a little way and then come back.

"Your Mr Blount was sent for and he took Skip back home, but it was no use. The dog just got free and went straight back to the grave. No matter what they did that dog always gave them the slip and went straight back to his master. And all this time he refused to eat. It wasn't long before he died too.

"Your Mr Blount asked the vicar if he could bury Skip along of his master in the same grave but the vicar wouldn't hear of it: 'The churchyard is consecrated ground,' he said. 'We don't even bury nonconformists there or suicides. It would be a desecration to bury a dog there.'

"So Mr Blount and some of Skipper's old friends from the pub took Skip and buried him lovingly down on the river bank close to the cottage.

"Now you would think that that was the end of the story but it wasn't."

Mr Guthrie knocked out his pipe and interrupted his wife.

"Do you really think you ought to tell the boy? It might give him nightmares."

"Course it won't. 'Tis a vitty little story – and anyway, the boy will be all curiosity now until he does hear it. That's true isn't it Roger?"

Roger didn't know whether he ought to stick up for Mr Guthrie or agree with Mrs Guthrie but he did want to hear the rest of the story even if it was a bit scary, so he nodded.

"Well then, neither Skipper nor Skip could rest easy in their graves. And the result of that was that any stormy night, if you walked down the lane from the churchyard to the river you would get the feeling that you weren't alone.

"As you drew closer to the river you would hear a dog howling. It sounded terrible in the wind. Back in the churchyard old Skipper heard it and used to rise ghost-like out of his grave. He would stomp down to the beach grumbling and cussing all the way.

" 'Poor old devil,' he would say. 'What did they want for to put you down there for? Why couldn't they put you with me? Hush boy. I be comin' to 'ee.'

"When he got to the beach the howling would stop and you'd see the old dog rise up squeaking and yapping with pleasure like a little old puppy, its tail wagging fit to drop off.

"The two of them would take a turn or two along the riverside and up to the cottage and then Skipper would see the dog back to its grave before making his own way back to the churchyard looking more upset and miserable than anyone could remember.

"This went on for the whole of the winter and there was a lot of talk about it down at the pub I can tell you. Eventually Mr Blount and two or three of Skipper's old friends, including the sexton, decided to take matters into their own hands.

"One dark night when there was no moon they went down to the riverbank and dug up Skip's little coffin. They carried it up to the churchyard and dug deep into Skipper's grave until they reached his coffin. Quietly and carefully they placed Skip on top of his master. Then they filled up the grave and slipped away to the back entrance of the pub and had a quiet celebration inside.

"Although the ghosts of Skipper and Skip can still be seen sometimes walking the lane to the river and taking a turn along the riverbank, the dog's howls have never been heard again. And even the churchyard seems to be a happier place for a bit of desecration."

Roger had listened spell-bound and wasn't at all scared when he went to bed. He found himself thinking about Tony, the spaniel he had known by the seaside. They had told him that when he left that last time, the dog had spent three whole nights outside his bedroom door. One day he would have a dog of his own, he thought, and with that happy thought he went to sleep.

# 21
# 'Dig for Victory'

After school one evening Roger took Jimmy Smith home with him to show him where he lived.

"This is my friend Jimmy," he told Mrs Guthrie. "He lives quite near to us."

"Hello Jimmy, where do you live then."

"24, King Charles Road."

"24. Let's see. That'll be Mrs Hancroft then." She seemed to know everybody.

"Yes," said Jimmy. "Can I take Roger and show him?"

"Course you can, only make sure as you'm not late home for tea young Roger."

The boys lived either side of Fort Park and the fort made a perfect place to play. That was their destination most evenings, and in the mornings they met up and went to school together.

Winter was over and the lengthening evenings of spring became the best part of every day. The impact of the war on Beddingford was minimal. Mr Guthrie listened to the news, sucking anxiously on his pipe and commenting as if they hadn't heard it too. In April he told them, "The Germans have invaded Denmark and Norway."

Mr Guthrie worked on the railway. This meant that he had to go to work at all sorts of odd times of day and night. It also meant that he was often free during the day time. He started to take Roger and Jimmy to his allotment down by the railway. The boys ran along the railway track leaping from sleeper to sleeper.

"Don't you never come down yer without me," said Mr

Guthrie. "I knows the times of the trains and you don't."

And when trains were coming he would draw the boys well to the side of the track.

"They trains suck up the air so much that, if you'm too close, they'll suck ee under and kill ee. So keep well back from the line," he warned them.

During the winter Mr Guthrie had been busy digging and his allotment was all ready for the first sowings of his vegetables. It was carefully divided into a number of different sections. Each year Mr Guthrie moved the different types of crop to a different section.

In one he planted potatoes. He showed the boys how to do it, and how deep they had to go and then he left them to plant them. As they planted he drew up the soil in ridges over the rows of potatoes.

"Us don't have to do it straight away but I always do. It shows me where the potatoes is and it protects them from the frost," he said.

Jimmy soon lost interest in the allotment but Roger was fascinated. He enjoyed the idea of growing your own food. It seemed much better than just going to the shops for it.

Mr Guthrie taught him to set onions in the ground without quite burying them. And they sowed all sorts of seed in a starter bed where Mr Guthrie had raked the soil very fine: cabbage, sprouts, cauliflower and broccoli; lettuce, carrots and beetroot.

In the months that followed he helped thin the carrots and the beetroot, leaving them to grow where they had been sown. He learned how to lift the lettuce and all the cabbage family of plants and to replant them, properly spaced out.

"Well done boy. Now us got to water them in. If us gives them a good watering now they'll get a good start. Then they won't need much more unless 'tis a real dry summer."

They watched over those infant plants and saw them take off. But other plants were taking off too.

"Yer boy. Do ee see all these weeds? Us must get rid of they."

He showed Roger how to use a hoe, but in places there was no escape from hand weeding on their knees. Roger enjoyed that rather more than Mr Guthrie.

"My old bones creaks when I has to get down like this yer. So you can spare me a bit if you will."

And as the plants grew the butterflies came and laid their eggs. These hatched out and the baby caterpillars began to crunch their way through Mr Guthrie's vegetables. But he was very watchful. He had already put jars in the ground half full of sugared water and with a few leaves of lettuce or cabbage.

"Those should catch the slugs for us and stop them from taking all our food," he had said. Now he took two jars and gave Roger one. "Come on boy. Us got to get rid of they caterpillars."

They worked steadily through the rows of vegetables picking off the caterpillars and then they took their jars full of wriggling creatures back to the shed. Mr Guthrie boiled up an old saucepan of water and they emptied the caterpillars in.

"That's an end to they," he said with satisfaction. "They don't feel no pain. They'm dead as soon as they hit the water."

He checked his plants every day and whenever the caterpillars were at all numerous he called Roger and they had a picking session.

"If you'm gwain to grow your own vegetables 'tis a constant battle boy. Us got to keep on top of they pests."

But other more serious battles were being fought in Europe. The news brought an explosion of anger.

" 'Tis just like the last war. They Germans has smashed through Holland and Belgium. Darned Maginot line weren't no use. They've just gone round it."

The speed of the German advance made people panicky. They seemed unstoppable. Everywhere they went they seemed to be winning resounding victories. And then came Dunkirk.

The effect was incredible. You would have thought that Britain had just won a glorious victory. An armada of small ships had set sail from the island fortress. A proud sea-faring nation had snatched the army from under the very noses of the enemy with brilliant seamanship and immense courage.

People hardly noticed that the British army was demoralised and defeated, without weapons or equipment. All that mattered was the simple fact that the army was home.

"We shall be all right now the army is back home," Mr Guthrie commented.

Somehow the nation's panic ebbed away and in these worst moments of disaster it was replaced by an iron resolve. In churches up and down the land thanks were given to God for the 'miracle' of Dunkirk. Clearly God was on the side of Great Britain and France – well Great Britain anyway.

A few boats had gone from Beddingford to Dunkirk and all of them were safely home.

"Let's go down to the river and have a look at the boats," said Roger.

"Cor look at that," exclaimed Jimmy when they saw how the boats had been riddled with bullets, chipped and holed but still safely home.

Churchill made the most of Dunkirk. He had taken over from Neville Chamberlain and now led a coalition government with the labour leader Clement Attlee as his deputy. People saw Churchill as the embodiment of British defiance, a British bulldog ready for the fight. For a boy like Roger defeat was unthinkable. Besides Alfie was in the Air Force now so they were bound to win.

Yet behind the bluff and bluster there was a widespread recognition that Britain was pretty helpless, a ripe plum ready for picking. But no matter how worried people were, life had to go on.

And for Roger that meant a birthday. He was nine. It promised to be the most ordinary birthday of his life. But he didn't mind that. He had never liked birthdays much. It was nice having presents of course. But he didn't like all the fuss. And he had never liked birthday parties. They always seemed to be organised by other people who made him invite 'friends' he didn't like and then made these all play lots of silly, sloppy games. When he had his eighth birthday he and Jimmy had slipped away after tea and gone off on their own leaving the rest to play. His mum hadn't been very pleased with him that day.

Now he was nine. Mr Guthrie was working in the morning so he wasn't there at breakfast time. Mrs Guthrie wished Roger a happy birthday and told him to bring Jimmy home for tea. That was all right. He hoped she wasn't going to invite anyone else or try to make them do things they didn't want to.

She packed him off to school and when school was over the two boys came straight back. Mr Guthrie was in his usual fireside chair, smoking his pipe. Mrs Guthrie was the other side of the fireplace knitting a jumper.

"Hello you two," said Mr Guthrie. "Had a decent day at school then?"

"Not bad," said Roger.

"Don't suppose anybody know'd it was your birthday did they?''

"Don't think so," said Roger. "No one said anything."

"Well there's a letter here from your dad and mum." He gave it to Roger.

There was a card which Mrs Guthrie put on the mantelpiece. And there were two letters. He read a typed letter from his dad first:

'Dea _oge_, I'm w_iting this lette_ on a typew_ite_ which has one lette_ missing. Because of the wa_ I can't have it _epai_ed.'

Then his dad went on at great length using as many words with r in them as he could. Roger had begun with his face screwed up in a sort of question mark, but once he got the hang of things he was soon giggling away.

"What's so funny?" asked Jimmy, irritated that he couldn't share the joke.

"My dad's typewriter is bust so his letter is coming out funny, that's all. I'll show you in a minute."

He finished reading, 'I hope you have a good bi_thday. We shall all be thinking of you. Give ou_ _ega_ds to M_ and M s Guth ie, Love, Dad.'

He passed the letter to Jimmy and went on to his Mother's letter. That was a much more sensible letter full of all the news from home. Alfie was being trained as a navigator in the RAF and it wouldn't be long before Eric went into the RAF too.

Attached to his Mother's letter there was a small envelope. He left that until last but when he finally opened it he was thrilled. It contained a ten shilling note.

"Cor." said Jimmy wide-eyed. He felt pretty envious. He had never had a ten shilling note in his life.

Nor had Roger until now. "Ten bob," he breathed. "Gosh." He was rich.

The Guthries had watched in considerable amusement, pleased that Roger had read the letters before opening the envelope. And they had read the letters too. But now:

"Come on boys. Let's have some tea then."

The tea table had been hidden beneath a cloth. Mrs Guthrie took it off and the boys gasped. They hadn't seen a tea like that for ages. Roger could almost hear his mother saying to him, "Now don't pig yourself and disgrace us all."

But he decided not to listen too hard.

Although they had to start with sandwiches or bread and jam, Mrs Guthrie didn't make them stay with bread. She let them go onto cakes or jelly or trifle straight away and they were both pretty full when she brought in a birthday cake with nine candles for Roger to blow out.

At last they decided they could eat no more and then Mr Guthrie went into a corner and pulled out two parcels.

"There boy. There's a birthday present for you and I thought you wouldn't mind if your pal Jimmy had one as well."

"Thank you Mr Guthrie. Thank you very much."

Each of them sat and untied the string and unwrapped the brown paper round it. String and paper were precious, so they gave them to Mrs Guthrie. But they could already see what Mr Guthrie had given them.

"Cor. Wow. Oh look. And arrows too."

Each of them had a bow and a quiver of arrows.

"Can we go and try them out?"

"Course you can. But be careful mind. No aiming at each other, nor at any other people either. Keep them well away from people."

"Yes Mr Guthrie – and thank you. They're wizard."

Out they went over to the fort. They slipped from bush to bush and tree to tree and then they attacked the German garrison and drove them out. They took control of the fort and then prepared for the inevitable counter attack, collecting up all the arrows they could find. The counter attack came and they fired their arrows, killing with every shot. When the arrows were gone they engaged in some desperate hand to hand shadow fighting before finally driving the Germans off. Their victory was complete.

When they tired of fighting Germans they just had target practice against a tree.

"D'you remember when you was Robin Hood and I was that stupid Will Scarlet?" asked Jimmy. "If we'd had these bows and arrows then we'd have had some fun I reckon.'

"Yeah," laughed Roger but then he thought of Mr Guthrie's words. How would they have had fun if they couldn't shoot at anyone. But Mr Guthrie was right. Shooting at people could be dangerous.

Those bows and a constant supply of new arrows from Mr Guthrie kept the two of them thoroughly happy right through the evenings until the summer holidays began. Not that Roger was often free in the evenings. The allotment saw to that.

At the end of May he helped Mr Guthrie set up a structure of eight foot sticks. And then in June, Mr Guthrie took a bag of runner beans he had kept from the year before and put them in water to soak overnight. The next day he and Roger planted them close to the sticks to grow all around them.

Meanwhile, back in the little gardens at the front and back of the house, Roger was learning to look after the flowers, especially the roses.

"Look at all that green-fly," Mr Guthrie would say. "You've got to watch that every day. 'Tis something you could do when you come home from school. Look see," and he drew his thumb and first two fingers up a rose shoot killing the green-fly as he went. Then he showed Roger his fingers and thumb all coloured green.

"Looks like proper smokers' fingers," he said, "but it all washes off."

Roger felt quite important taking on these jobs, and he learned to keep an eye open for the milkman too.

The milkman came up the road every morning with his horse pulling the milk float. Quite often the horse dropped a pile of manure for the garden and Roger rushed out with a shovel and a bucket to collect it before anyone else could. He was determined that Mr Guthrie's garden would be the best manured in all the road.

By the time summer came the allotment was full of growing plants, some of them ready for eating. And at home the little front and back gardens were a picture.

That autumn the government put up big posters everywhere saying 'Dig for Victory'. Roger felt proud that he had been helping Mr Guthrie. It was all helping to win the war. And the events of that June had shown very clearly that the war was going to take some winning.

# 22

# The Submarine

On June the tenth Mr Guthrie heard on the news that Italy had joined the war on the side of Germany.

"Typical," he snorted. "That Mussolini waits until all the fighting's done and then joins in to pick up the spoils. Well one day he's going to learn that he's picked the wrong side. You mark my words."

But they didn't. They were getting used to his minor explosions and didn't pay any attention any more.

Four days later the Germans entered Paris in triumph. The French had surrendered their capital city without a fight in order to preserve the city.

Surprisingly enough there was a good deal of sympathy for their decision. Some people denounced the French for their cowardice but a surprising number thought that their decision had been sensible and right. For the first time nine-year-old Roger found himself face to face with questions about war. Was it always right to fight? Did fighting always produce the answer to problems?

The questions were easily dismissed at the time. It was obvious to almost everyone then that Britain had got to fight Hitler and Mussolini to the bitter end, but the seeds of those questions had been sown and in adult life they would return to haunt him again and again.

Soon afterwards the French government gave up the struggle. Now Britain stood alone. Was the situation hopeless? It should have been but it didn't feel that way.

f

"All we need is a bit of time," said Mr Guthrie. "We always start off losing wars but we always win in the end. That Hitler hasn't bargained on the British Empire. Give us a bit of time and we'll teach those Jerries a lesson they won't forget in a hurry. And as for them Eyeties, they're just a joke."

At school the summer term came to an end and the holidays began. Quite often Mrs Guthrie and Mrs Hancroft gave the boys sandwiches so that they could go to the seaside. Sometimes they took Mrs Hancroft's terrier Bill.

He loved it, running across the fields and sniffing in all the hedges. But when they got home they always had to go through his coat to see if they could find any sheep ticks.

Mrs Hancroft used to light a cigarette and give it to Jimmy so that he could burn the ticks off. He quite liked that because it gave him the chance of a puff or two. AND Mrs Hancroft gave him a halfpenny a tick.

They preferred walking to going on the bus. That was so slow. But sometimes one of them would say, "I've got some money for the bus fare. Shall we go by bus and walk back, or shall we walk there and bus back?"

They nearly always walked there and came back on the bus when they were tired.

That bus. To save petrol it ran on gas and had a huge container-trailer behind it. Whenever they got to a steep hill all the passengers had to get off. Otherwise the bus couldn't get to the top. At the top of the hill all the passengers climbed aboard again. That three mile journey up hill and down dale took ages.

So the boys preferred the footpath over the hills. When they came in sight of the sea there was a long sandy beach to the right. But that was covered in barbed wire and full of mines so they couldn't play there.

To the left was a long expanse of rocks and rock pools. And on the front near the rocks there was a long line of beach huts.

Miss Binns and Miss Smythe had hired one of those huts and told the children at school that they would be there every day. So any children who could come to the seaside could come to the hut.

"Race yer," yelled Jimmy, beginning to run.

At first he left Roger behind because he was faster, but he soon grew puffed and then Roger would gradually catch up. Who

122

arrived first depended on where they started racing from. And when they arrived there were always some of their friends there, and Margaret was always there.

"Are you coming for a swim boys?" asked Miss Smythe.

Roger was always keener than Jimmy. Thank goodness for Barbara making him learn. Jimmy couldn't swim and didn't want to learn even though Miss Smythe was teaching some of the others. Margaret had already learned. But like it or not, down they all went across the rocks to a spot where the rocks formed a kind of circle and made a natural swimming pool.

"Who is going to be first in?" shouted Miss Smythe. "I'll beat the lot of you." But she made sure that she never did.

Parts of the pool were shallow enough for the non-swimmers and part of it was deep enough for them to dive off the rocks. Even though he couldn't swim, Jimmy liked diving but he made sure he came up where he could grab the rocks at the edge.

Splashing, swimming, messing about, the morning was soon gone. Then they all went up to the beach hut and ate their sandwiches.

"Swap you," was a constant cry but neither Roger nor Jimmy wanted to swap. They knew there weren't many sandwiches as good as theirs.

After lunch, Roger and Jimmy used to go off on their own. The teachers had bought a couple of prawning nets and a canvas bag. The boys used to borrow them and head off over the rocks. When they found a good pool for prawns they would lower their nets very gently and draw them along under the ledges and as close as they could to all the nooks and crannies.

"Got anything?"

"Yeah, but I'd better get all this old sea-weed out first."

The prawns hopped about trying to escape. But it wasn't difficult to catch them now they were in the net.

"Got four that time and two crabs."

"Put the crabs in that other pool. We don't want to catch them every time."

They moved from pool to pool gradually building up their bag of prawns.

"What's that?"

"It's a lobster," replied Roger. "Look, that's its hole. Cover the hole with your net, quick."

The lobster had seen them. Very carefully it was moving itself backwards trying to back into its hideaway hole. But Jimmy thrust his net down just in time. The lobster shot forward.

Roger lowered his net carefully into the pool and began to manoeuvre the lobster towards an open corner of the pool. Time after time he thought he had it trapped but each time it shot past his net just at the last moment. Jimmy was getting frustrated.

"Here let me have a go. You're no good."

But he dared not move his net from the lobster's escape hole.

"Come and hold my net and let me have a go."

"Sh.' Roger was not to be deflected.

He hit on the idea of working from the bottom and drawing the lobster up towards the surface. The net and the lobster seemed to glide through the pool, always at the same distance from one another. Then the lobster could go no further and prepared to make its dash. Roger waited. Jimmy could hardly contain himself.

For a while both lobster and net were still, but Roger was inching his net very slowly upwards. He angled it so that its bar rose to the surface. Then with a mighty heave he hoisted net and lobster out onto the rocks.

"You got it. You got it," screamed Jimmy.

They both looked at it and then Jimmy said as casually as he could, "You gonna put it in the bag then?"

Roger looked at its fearsome claw and answered, "You can if you like."

But Jimmy didn't like. Eventually they decided to take it back to the hut in the net.

"What on earth have you got there?" asked Miss Binns as they all crowded round to have a look.

"It's a lobster," said Roger.

"Go and get some sea water," said Miss Smythe.

Both Roger and Jimmy took buckets down and collected water from a rock pool and Miss Smythe put on a saucepan to boil. When it was boiling she took a tablespoon and gave it to Roger while the others looked on.

"You keep it busy with that spoon and I'll pick it up," she said.

So while Roger kept pretending to prod it with the spoon and the lobster clawed at the spoon, Miss Smythe drew back the net and picked it up behind its claw before dropping it into the boiling

124

water. A couple of minutes later she lifted it out and said to Roger and Jimmy, "You'd better take that home with you to show to your hostesses. Now let's have some tea. Put your prawns into the saucepan."

So they emptied their bag into the saucepan and it wasn't long before the prawns had turned pink and were ready to eat. That evening the boys went to Roger's home first and showed their lobster to Mrs Guthrie.

"Oh my dear soul, whatever next. You've caught a lobster have ee."

Roger told her that they had managed to catch it between them.

"You'd better take it home with ee Jimmy. Mrs Hancroft will want to see that."

Roger was not too pleased but he realised that it was only fair. So Jimmy took it home with him and boasted how he had caught it all on his own.

But he did share his lobster sandwiches with Roger the following day.

The boys never tired of the rock pools. They were full of tiny fish, crabs, anemones and sea-weed and sometimes larger fish like dog fish were trapped when the tide went out. And there were caves in the cliffs as well so the boys never got bored.

Up above the cliffs on the bracken covered hills there were lots of narrow footpaths that were hardly ever used except by the deer. One of them led to an old broken-down coastguard look-out post that wasn't used at all any more. It became Roger's and Jimmy's secret den and reminded them of old Sam's place. He had taught them more than they realised.

Bit by bit they managed to collect all sorts of treasures including an old, battered saucepan which Roger found at the allotments and a very worn prawning net left behind on the beach. They patched up the prawning net with string. It wasn't very good but it was better than nothing. They stored all their treasures in a sack and hid it in the bracken.

It was rare for them to see anyone. If they did, they simply hid themselves in the bracken where no one could see them. The smell of the bracken was marvellous.

Down below on the pebble beach they often found driftwood which they collected and stuffed under the beach hut. Then, when no one was around, they put it in a sack and carried it up to their den for firewood. And they dragged pieces of timber up that took their combined strength and several goes. These they set around the den walls for seats.

They made a fireplace in one corner where there was a hole in the wall but they never found a pipe for the smoke, so it often blew into the den with the wind coming through the hole, instead of finding its way out. They managed to cook prawns on a fire there though, so they were pretty pleased.

Sometimes they felt like smugglers and sometimes coast-guards. Jimmy had a pair of binoculars with glass in only one eye, but that was pretty good. One evening he was peering out to sea. Away in the distance the coast curved round and back again making a very wide channel. On a fine day you could see the coast on the other side. One evening Jimmy shouted, "Hey. What's that? Roger come and look."

Jimmy pointed across the channel to the cliffs the other side but it was dusk and Roger couldn't see anything. Jimmy handed over the binoculars and pointed again. Roger focussed the single eye-piece and moved his gaze along the bottom of the cliffs. Then he stopped. What was that. It was a bit blurred but could it be? It looked like a submarine.

"Can you see it?" whispered Jimmy as if someone on the boat could hear. "What do you think it is? It's a U boat isn't it? It's the invasion. The Jerries have come. Come on. We've got to warn someone."

He was hopping up and down like a mad thing. Roger peered some more, and then looked without the binoculars. Now that he knew where to look he could make it out without their help. It certainly looked like a submarine. But if it was it was probably one of ours.

Jimmy was looking through the binoculars again. "It is. It is. It's a U boat. We've got to tell someone."

"Nah," said Roger. "It's probably one of ours."

"But s'pose it isn't," answered Jimmy. "S'pose it IS a U boat. An' s'pose it's the invasion. We've gotta warn people."

"P'raps you're right," said Roger. "We'll go and tell the police. Just in case."

So the two boys set off as fast as they could run, right across the coast path and down to the seaside village. They ran through the village to the police house with the dim blue light outside.

126

They hammered on the door. And then suddenly, they got colly-wobbles. They were still trying to make up their minds whether to stay and see it through, or to run away and say nothing to anyone, when the policeman came to the door buttoning up his jacket as he came.

" 'Ello boys," he said. "What's the matter then."

"Please sir, we've seen a submarine and we thought it might be the invasion."

The policeman kept his face as serious and straight as he could.

"You've seen a submarine eh. And where do you think you saw it then?"

"Across by the other coast," Roger told him.

"Bit dark to see anything across there i'nt it?"

"We were up on the hills and it was only just beginning to get dark."

"And I've got binoculars," added Jimmy.

"Ah," said the policeman. "An' just what did you see?"

"Well it wasn't all that clear. But it was a long grey shape under the cliffs and it looked just like a submarine."

"Hm. You'd better come on in."

So in they went and were introduced to the policeman's wife.

"Betsy," said the policeman, "see if you can find these boys something to eat and drink. They think they've seed a submarine. I'd better phone through to Beddingford just in case they really 'ave."

"So you've seed a submarine have ee," said Betsy. And then she switched the conversation straight onto another tack.

"Do your mothers let ee stay out this late at night? Where do ee live?"

"Please missus," answered Jimmy, "we're evacuees. We don't live with our mothers."

"We live in Beddingford," added Roger and they gave Betsy their addresses.

"Albert," shouted Betsy. "Before you get off thick phone give the Inspector thoose boys addresses. Their volks will be worried sick about they." Then she turned to the boys and said, "I expect you could eat some chips couldn't ee?"

"Oh yes please," they chorused.

Meanwhile Albert was talking to his Inspector: "Of course sir, there's probably nothing in it, but they seem two decent lads so I thought perhaps we ought to check it out."

"Yes. Thank you Robinson," the Inspector answered. "I'll alert the Navy. You'll see to the boys."

"Yes sir. Excuse me sir."

"Yes."

"Sir. The boys are evacuees living in Beddingford and the last bus has gone."

"Oh."

"Sir, my Betsy could find beds for the boys if someone could tell their hostesses where they be."

"Yes. Very well. Give their addresses to our duty sergeant and he'll attend to it – oh and thank your wife."

So the boys ate their chips and drank dandelion and burdock which fizzed right up their nose and then they went to bed. They were asleep in no time but in the middle of the night Mr Robinson came and woke them up.

"Yer boys. Come and have a look at this." He took them through into his own bedroom and Betsy wrapped blankets round them while they all stood at the window watching. Out in the channel there were flashes and booms and bangs and the grey shapes of ships. They couldn't make out what happened but after a while there was silence.

The next morning the phone rang and then Betsy came hurrying upstairs.

"Come on boys. You must get up quickly and have some breakfast. There's something for you to see."

They got up and washed and had their breakfast and then a police car arrived. Constable Robinson and Betsy and the two boys all crowded in and the car drove to Beddingford to the riverside. Quite a crowd had gathered. The police took the boys through the crowd right onto the river front.

Coming up the river were two ships. One of them was a grey naval corvette and one of them was a grey German submarine with British sailors on board. It looked pretty badly battered.

The two ships drew up alongside the quay. Naval guards stood prepared on the quay and then, from the corvette came a seemingly endless stream of German sailors. They looked sullen and angry. The crowd booed.

They were marched away under guard to the station to be taken away to prison camps. The boys felt very funny inside – sort of very big and very little all at the same time. A police officer and a naval officer came across to them.

The naval officer said, "We want to thank you for reporting that submarine last night. It was damaged and hoped to hide long enough to do enough repairs to enable it to get home. But thanks to you two it won't cause our shipping any more trouble. Well done." – and he shook them both by the hand.

Fortunately the boys didn't hear the officer telling the Police Inspector that they already knew where the U boat was before the boys' report came in and their ships were already on their way to capture it.

That evening there was a programme on the wireless in which all the national anthems of all the countries fighting against Germany were being played, one after the other. Roger had gone to bed early but he could hear them very clearly up in his room. He got up on his bed and stood to attention until the very last one was finished. He felt so proud that he was helping to win the war.

# 23

# The Fishermen of England

After Dunkirk, Mr Guthrie had commented that with the army safely back home, all we needed was a bit of time. If he had lived with Roger's parents he might have felt that time was the one thing Hitler was not going to provide.

In July the blitz began in earnest. All through July, August and well into September the bombers droned across the skies and the bombing reached terrible proportions. Around George and Lilian's home almost every house suffered damage of one kind or another. Their own house did not escape. They had a few ceilings down and windows and doors blown in, but they counted themselves lucky that the damage was so slight.

At the end of the summer term, Roger and Margaret's school had gone back home but some of the children had stayed. The younger ones were simply absorbed into the council school whose buildings their school had shared. But a few of the older ones, including Roger and Jimmy were to go early to Gerry's school, the Grammar School from home. Miss Smythe and Miss Binns had stayed on to give them some sort of care through the summer holidays, but come September they would be returning home too. When they heard of the blitz they were glad to be in Beddingford still, and felt that a whole lot of wrong decisions had been made.

For Beddingford remained a quiet, peaceful place to live. Apart from the rationing and the blackout and more and more people in uniform, the war hardly seemed to touch the town. Just occasionally a bomber strayed their way and dropped its bombs, but it was very rare.

And then one night a bomber dropped a land mine. People heard a huge explosion, but no one seemed to know where it was. Out in the country somewhere they reckoned, and when there were no more explosions they thought no more about it.

Early next morning the first workers' bus of the day set out from the bus depot empty. It trundled merrily along the main road. With its lights shaded because of the black-out, visibility was almost zero. The driver drove straight into the land-mine crater and his bus almost disappeared. He was badly bruised and knocked out for a minute or two, but he wasn't seriously hurt.

When Roger and Jimmy heard about it they went to have a look.

'Blimey," said Jimmy and added, "I wonder if there's any shrapnel anywhere."

So they went on a shrapnel hunt. But there were no anti-aircraft guns in the area so the only bits were from the mine and they didn't find any of those.

The news was full of the blitz and all the dogfights between the RAF and the Luftwaffe. Mr Guthrie decided that he would take Roger to the cinema so that they could see what was on the Gaumont News. Jimmy went with them.

Seeing the news at the cinema, in those days before TV, gave them a tremendous sense of the excitement of the Battle of Britain but they were too young for the seriousness of it all to register – and too far away. They started listening to the news on the wireless. Huge numbers of German planes were being shot down. What did it matter if the details and the claims were wildly exaggerated. Although the Luftwaffe damaged or destroyed three million homes by November 1940, it was the RAF which gradually won the battle of the skies.

And little by little people realised the fact.

At Dunkirk the Navy had given Britain renewed hope and pride. Now the RAF brought a renewal of self-confidence. The Battle of Britain had given people a taste of victory. One day the Army's turn would come.

Only the best of these things, the most optimistic and the most hopeful and confident, filtered through to the boys and fed their imaginations. If it hadn't been for the radio and the cinema, and Alfie and Eric in the RAF. Roger would hardly have thought

131

about the war. Life was so normal.

When he and Jimmy went down to the river to watch the fishermen the war could have been a million miles away.

Three fishermen worked together just above the bridge. One of them stood in the riverside mud holding the end of a long seine net. The other two were in a rowing boat. One rowed round in a big circle while the other one stood in the stern and paid out the net until the circle was complete. Then he jumped out into the mud. The two men holding the ends of the net began to haul it in.

"Look at them," cried Jimmy.

As the circle of net grew smaller and smaller, fish began to jump to try to escape. The water inside the net was a swirling mass of fish crowded together and jumping desperately. The men pulled their net onto the bank and began putting the fish into buckets.

"Come on you two. Come and give us a hand," one of the fishermen shouted.

Jimmy got into it straight away. He and his dad had fished for eels before the war and he was used to the feel of wet, wriggling creatures. Roger wasn't so sure. He had watched old Sam fishing but he'd always avoided actually holding the fish. Now he had to.

The fishermen watched him with amusement. "Go on boy. That's the way. The little ones goes back into the river. They id'n' no use now but us'll catch them again one day. The rest goes into the buckets except for the biggest. You can leave they to us."

Slowly he got over his distaste for the job and began to get on with it, though he would never be as quick as Jimmy. He was like quicksilver.

'Well done boys. Do ee want to come out in the boat?"

"Ooh, yes please sir."

"Come on then."

A fisherman lifted first Jimmy and then Roger into the boat.

"Now you sit there. What's your name?"

"Jimmy Smith sir."

"Right. You take hold of this oar and just hold him with the blade out of the water. An' what's your name sonny?"

"Roger Wallace sir."

"Right Roger. You sit there and hold this one like young Jimmy there."

The boat had wobbled a lot as they got themselves sorted out

132

but now it settled still in the water.

"Now," said the fisherman, "when I say 'pull' you must both dip the blade of the oar into the water and pull hard. Then, when I say 'rest', you push down on your hands to lift the blade free of the water. Ready?"

"Yes sir," they chimed.

"Pull."

Roger dipped his oar in. It went so deep that he couldn't pull it through the water. Jimmy didn't even get his oar below the surface. It scudded across the top of the water sending spray right across everybody in the boat and sending Jimmy flying over backwards into the bottom of the boat.

"Well boy, you've caught a proper crab," said the fisherman.

"Where?" asked Jimmy excitedly and the oarsman laughed.

"Not a real crab you ninny. That's what us calls it when you make a big splash like that."

They got ready again but this time the oarsman held his rough, strong hands over the hands of the boys and showed them how to dip and pull, dip and pull, until they began to get the hang of it. Then he let them row without his help.

The boat twisted and turned, first this way, then that, then round in a circle and back again as first one boy and then the other rowed the stronger.

That poor boat went everywhere except in a straight line and the boys caught plenty more 'crabs' and got themselves thoroughly soaked in the process. But little by little they learned how to row properly and before long they were quite skilful.

Was it as a reward for their help or for the laughs they gave them? For one reason or the other the fishermen gave the boys some fish to take home for supper.

"What on earth have you been doing?" exclaimed Mrs Guthrie.

Roger gave her the fish and told her all about his evening.

"Well next time you go you must wear your Saturday clothes," she said. "But I must say as we shall enjoy thoose fish. You just get upstairs and have a good hot bath while I get us some supper."

# 24

# The Quarry Gang

When the boys went to school at the Grammar School they found themselves in another shared building. The premises belonged to Beddingford Grammar. One week they had the school in the mornings and the next week in the afternoons. Overcrowding was desperate. Gerry's class was out in the school cricket pavilion.

Roger and Jimmy found themselves in the 1st form, full of eleven-year-old boys. No concessions were made to the half dozen nine or ten year olds who had come from Roger's school. Roger found that there was a great deal that he didn't understand, especially in maths.

But he liked English and History with old 'One Lung'. 'One Lung' had been gassed in the first world war. He wouldn't let anyone else dust the blackboard. He always did it himself so that as little dust as possible was spread about. And no matter how cold it was, he always had windows open.

Boys who were called to the front had to remember to keep their distance.

"Wallace, bring your history essay please."

Roger went to the front and 'One Lung' began to mark it. Roger edged forward to see what he was writing in the margin.

One Lung's hand pushed him away. "Don't breathe your filthy breath down my clean neck," he said.

Jimmy was a tougher, harder boy than Roger even though he wasn't quite as big. He was thin and wiry and very quick. When he wasn't with Roger he spent his time with a gang of grammar school boys two or three years older than himself.

They called themselves 'the Quarry Gang' because their head-quarters was an old, disused quarry. A steep, narrow pathway led up the side of the quarry and at the top there was a flat ledge about the size of a large living room. It had been covered with brambles and bushes but the boys had cleared the centre completely, leaving only the bushes on the quarry edge. These formed a perfect screen so that from the bottom of the quarry you couldn't see their den at all.

There were about twenty boys in the gang and they roamed around Beddingford together. They had a lot of fun together, fought with Beddingford boys, 'borrowed' boats without permission, scrumped apples from orchards, but they didn't do much harm.

However, Beddingford wasn't used to such gangs. Some people were frightened by the sight of a crowd of teen-aged boys roaming the streets together. Shopkeepers were afraid that the boys would steal their goods (and sometimes the boys did). Gradually the gang got a bad reputation.

Jimmy asked if he could bring Roger to join the gang. At first they said 'no'. Roger was too young. But Jimmy was a useful gang member himself and he kept on asking so eventually it was decided to give Roger a try. But before he could join the gang he had to be tested.

One evening he was rowing on the river with Jimmy and one of the fishermen. Another boat came by with two boys in it. "Race yer to the bridge," they yelled.

"Come on," said Jimmy. "We'll beat them easy."

"Yes," said the fisherman. "Reckon you will. Pull away then."

So Roger and Jimmy bent to the oars and slowly began to overhaul the other boat. The fisherman helped because he steered the boat into those parts of the river where the current ran strongest. Well before the bridge they were level and they shot underneath clear winners. Roger didn't know it but he had passed the first test.

A few days later Jimmy said, "There's a cross country run for the third form boys tonight. I'm going to join in and see how many I can beat. You coming?"

"But we're not allowed to," answered Roger.

"Who's to stop us? They start in the school. We'll join them outside the gates and pack up when we get back to the gates. I bet we can beat a lot of those boys."

"Course we can," said Roger. "All right. Let's have a go."

So when the run began two small first form boys joined in. But not for long. It was a hot, sticky evening and Roger had left his singlet with the rest of his clothes so that he was running only in shorts and gym shoes. They had run less than a mile when they met a policeman cycling the other way. He came to an abrupt halt, almost falling off his bike in the process.

"You. You boy," and he pointed at Roger. "What do ee think you'm about of? Tidn decent,.rinnin around with no clothes on. You go back to school and put your vest back on. I don't know what the world's comin' to."

So Roger and Jimmy had to turn back and by the time they were ready to start again it wasn't worth bothering. So that was the end of that. Roger was bitterly disappointed. He had never been on a cross country run before and he was just beginning to enjoy himself when they were stopped.

A week later there was another run for the third form and this time the two boys joined in without interruption.

Jimmy soon began to wish he hadn't. He was very good over one hundred yards and he could run round town for ever, but running just for running – that was something else. Meanwhile Roger was enjoying himself. He felt as if he could go on for ever. He saw other boys already beginning to struggle and he felt strong. This was good fun.

Jimmy panted, "One of my laces has come undone. You go on. I'll catch you up later."

So Roger ran on and Jimmy slipped through the hedge for a rest. The run took the boys out of the heights of Beddingford along a footpath over the hills and through some woods and then curved back along a country lane to another footpath and then back to the road to school. Roger and Jimmy hadn't started too fast but now that he was on his own Roger increased his speed without realising it. He began to overtake one boy after another.

As he was running along the final road that led back to school Jimmy slipped back through the hedge and caught up with him. He was surprisingly fresh and chattered away while Roger kept his breath for running. Without thinking what they were doing they ran straight into the school, racing one another over the last stretch.

"Well done boys," said one of the masters. "Straight into the showers with you."

The winning boy was a thirteen year old called Ledstock. He was also leader of the Quarry Gang. He watched the two come in, saw them through the showers and out of the school safely.

"Well done you two," he said, "especially you youngster."

"Cor. Did you hear that?" Roger said to Jimmy. "He's super. I'm going to get myself properly in training so's I can race them all – well all except Ledstock. I don't suppose I'll ever beat him."

What Roger didn't know was that he had passed test number two. Test number three took place when he was on his way home through Fort Park one evening. He was running along with a ball at his feet as usual when another boy came running up behind him, kicked the ball away, ran after it and picked it up, and began to run off with it.

Roger went after him. " 'Ere gimme my ball."

"Findin's keepin's," shouted the boy and dodged behind a bush.

"Gi' us it," shouted Roger. He caught the boy who was not really trying to get away and sailed into him, fists flying.

One of his punches hurt and it made the boy angry. He was a good deal bigger than Roger and he came back at him fiercely. Roger was still concentrating on his ball. He dived for the hand that held it but the boy dropped it and grabbed Roger instead. The two of them began to wrestle. Roger knew he couldn't win but he was determined to get his ball back. He wriggled free, grabbed his ball and started to run. The next thing he knew the bigger boy had rugby-tackled him and he had gone crashing to the ground. He twisted but the bigger boy was on top and slowly got his arms pinned to the ground. Roger managed to tip him off again and again but he always got back on top and at last he had Roger in a grip like a vice.

"Gotcha! You give in and gimme my ball."

" 'Taint your ball. An' I won't give in."

The bigger boy ground his chin into Roger's chest. It hurt like hell. "Now give in."

"No," panted Roger.

The bigger boy moved to put his knee on Roger's arm muscle but Roger wriggled free just at the right moment, punched the boy in the pills and got away. He ran for home as hard as he could go.

The boy made no attempt to follow. As Ledstock and a few others appeared from the fort he held his pills and felt an awful pain in his stomach.

"Well, he's not a bad little fighter," said Ledstock. "There's just the one test to go. You bring him down to the quarry Jimmy and we'll see what he's like at climbing."

So the very next evening Jimmy took Roger to the quarry. "I've found a smashin' place," he said. "I'll take you there after dinner."

When they got to the quarry there was a rope hanging from a tree at the top.

"Cor look at that," said Jimmy. "Let's have a swing."

He scrambled up the side of the quarry until he could grab the rope and then pushed away and swung round and round banging on his chest and shouting the Tarzan challenge. He and Roger took turns and had quite a bit of fun. Then Jimmy started to climb up the rope. He was almost like a monkey. Up and up and up he went until he reached the tree. Then he shouted down, "Cor it's super up 'ere. Come on up."

Roger looked and felt sure he couldn't make it. He wasn't half as good at climbing as Jimmy. But of course he didn't want to say so. He looked around and noticed the path. It was a bit steep but it was better than the rope. He shouted back, "I'll come up that way and see you at the top."

"That doesn't reach the top," lied Jimmy. "I've tried it."

"Well I'll just see how far it goes," Roger answered and began to trot towards the path.

"You're scared," yelled Jimmy.

"No I'm not."

"Well come up the rope then."

"I don't want to. I don't feel like it."

"Garn. You are scared. Who'd 'ave thought Roger Wallace was a cowardy custard."

Roger was angry with Jimmy for taunting him and he was angry with himself because he knew he *was* scared.

"I'm not scared," he said. "I just want to see where the path goes."

"Oo jer fink you're kiddin'," shouted Jimmy. "Yer can't climb it and yer scared ter try."

"Course I can climb it," answered Roger angrily.

138

"Well go on then. Climb it. I dare you."

Once again the challenge had been thrown down and there was no escape. A dare was a dare.

Roger gripped the rope with his hands and caught it between his feet the way they had been taught to climb in the gym. Slowly, laboriously, he began to haul himself up. Why couldn't he climb like Jimmy? Higher and higher he went. His arms began to ache. He felt they wouldn't pull him any more. He got a good grip with his feet and rested letting his feet take the weight. Then he looked down.

He shut his eyes and felt suddenly sick and weak. It was such a long way. Suppose he fell. He'd kill himself.

Jimmy had been watching him all the way as had all the other members of the gang. Some of them remembered how scared they had been on the rope and how hard it had been to get to the top.

"Don't look down," called Jimmy. "You haven't far to go. Just look up at me."

Roger looked up. It was true. He hadn't far to go, but could he manage even that?

"I don't think I can make it," he gasped. "I'm not as good a climber as you are. I think I'd better go down."

"Course yer can make it," Jimmy said, "and when you've done it once you'll find it much easier the next time. Go on. 'ave a go."

"Have you done it before then?" asked Roger.

Jimmy realised that he had nearly let the cat out of the bag. "Yeah," he said. "The rope was here when I found the quarry. I tried it then — and it was much harder the first time. Come on. You can do it."

Roger looked up at Jimmy and heaved himself up again. His arms felt better for their rest. One pull and a rest. One pull and a rest. Slowly but surely up he went. Thank goodness he could grip so well with his feet. He kept his eyes on Jimmy. He was getting closer and closer. But somehow it was hard to focus. Jimmy was all misty. Crikey his arms didn't half hurt.

"Come on," shouted Jimmy excitedly. "You've made it. You're there," and he reached out and touched Roger to prove it. Then he moved himself back out of the way.

Roger hauled himself up again and got a hand on a branch of the tree. Then he got a foot on a branch where it joined the trunk.

But he couldn't let go of the rope. He couldn't let go. He was stuck.

"You've done it," yelled Jimmy. "Come on. You've done it."

Roger held the tree with all his strength, swung himself and grabbed at the tree with his other hand. He clung on and then pulled himself onto the tree and rested. Slowly he became aware of a lot of shouting and cheering. He looked round and saw a lot of boys in a clearing. He scrambled down the tree and Jimmy hauled in the rope.

"Well done Wallace," said Ledstock, shaking him by the hand. "You didn't know it but you've been on trial. You passed the rowing test and the running test. Then you had a fighting test with Maclean and left him with sore balls." (Everybody had a good laugh and Maclean grinned and shook his fist). "Now you've passed the climbing test – just. But you'd better improve your climbing. So now you can join us and be a member of the Quarry Gang if you want to that is."

Roger looked around him. All these boys were older than he was – except Jimmy. And they were letting him join their gang.

"Oh yes please," he said proudly.

"Then you've got to swear never to tell anyone our name or where we meet or what we do. It's the vow of loyalty and silence."

"I swear all right," answered Roger.

Say after me: "I swear."

"I swear."

"Never to tell"

"Never to tell"

"one single thing"

"one single thing"

"about the Quarry Gang."

"about the Quarry Gang."

"Good. Now shake hands with me and with all the rest to bind you to your vow."

So Roger shook Ledstock's hand and then went right round the circle. He felt very excited and very proud. But in fact, joining the gang was the worst thing he could have done, although it was not until the spring of 1941 that matters were to come to a head. While Germany was invading Yugoslavia and Greece and launching its African offensive, Beddingford was the scene of a battle which had very serious results for Roger.

# 25

# The Battle

The members of the Quarry Gang were older than Roger. Because of it they stayed out later at night than he was supposed to. The people who looked after Jimmy didn't seem to mind what time he came in at night but Mr and Mrs Guthrie expected Roger to be in at 9.00. He tried to remember but after he joined the gang he was always late. Mostly he got home between 9.15 and 9.30 but sometimes he was as late as 10.00. The Guthries were worried about him and they ticked him off severely but they hadn't the heart actually to punish him.

However, when things didn't improve and the tickings off just made Roger bad-tempered, they felt they ought to report what was happening to Roger's form teacher Mr Westaway. But it was the battle which brought things to a head.

Unknown to the Quarry Gang, some of the Beddingford boys had been following them and had discovered their headquarters. So one evening when the gang members began to arrive they found that the Beddingford boys were already there and when they tried to climb up they were bombarded with mud pies.

Ledstock drew them back round a corner of the road. He picked out a small group.

"We'll climb round behind them," he said, "and attack from behind. It won't take us all that long. Meanwhile you keep them busy from in front so that they don't realise what's happening."

So the main group attacked again with whoops and shouts and they pressed their attack so hard that one or two of them actually managed to get to the top. But once they were up there, they were so heavily outnumbered that they hadn't a hope. The fighting went on for about twenty minutes and then suddenly there was a terrific shout as Ledstock and his group attacked from behind.

Now the larger group managed to scramble up the quarry face and soon the open space on top was a mass of bodies of boys boxing, wrestling, struggling and fighting for all they were worth. The Quarry Gang was larger than the Beddingford group and gradually began to get the better of things. After a long struggle the Beddingford leader shouted:

"Come on boys. Us'll come back another day – only more of us."

With that he half ran, half fell down the quarry face and ran off. His friends went with him and the boys of the Quarry Gang followed, chasing and cheering and jeering. Then they turned and cheered one another, slapping each other on the back and telling each other what a great gang they were. It took some time before Roger had sobered up enough to start wondering what time it was and whether he ought to get home.

When he finally got home it was half past ten. Mrs Guthrie let him in and looked at him in horror.

"What on earth have you been doing? Where did you get that eye? And just look at your clothes. They're filthy and look at that tear.

"Dad," she called to Mr Guthrie, "just look at this boy. What be us gwain to do with 'n."

Mr Guthrie was sitting by the fire, smoking his pipe and reading. He looked at Roger and said, "Well. what have ee been up to then?"

"Just having a bit of a fight," answered Roger sulkily.

"Quite a bit of a fight if you asks me," answered Mr Guthrie. "Well us be gettin' proper fed up with ee all thoose late nights and now this. 'Tidn' niver right. You go an' have a bath an' get to bed. I shall come with ee to school tomorrow an' speak to your teacher about ee. Go on with ee. Get up they stairs."

So Roger had his bath and got to bed and the following morning Mr Guthrie went with him to school. He was introduced to Mr Benfleet, Roger's form master.

"Us thinks the boy has got in with a bad crowd of boys. He keeps coming home late at night. Last night was particular bad, and he'd been in a fight. Well you can see that. Only got to look

142

at his black eye.

"He's a good enough boy normally an' us be very fond of 'n. But us tells 'n off an' ee don't take no notice. If you speak to 'n perhaps that'll do the trick."

"Thank you for telling us," Mr Benfleet replied. "I'm sorry to hear that you've been having such trouble. Just you leave young Roger to us. We'll soon sort him out."

So Mr Guthrie went home. Mr Benfleet did nothing himself. He simply went to the headmaster and told him, "Young Wallace is causing trouble. He's got in with some bad company and was mixed up in a fight last night. I'm afraid that his host and hostess can't cope with him any longer."

If the Guthries had heard him they would have been horrified. All they wanted from the school was a bit of help. Instead they lost a boy they really cared about. The headmaster said, "Don't worry. Just send the boy to me and I'll deal with him. I've got just the place for him. Do you know Mr Hilton the solicitor? His two maids have just joined the land army and he wants two evacuees to take their place."

"Literally to take their place?" asked Mr Benfleet.

"Oh yes, quite literally if I know Hilton. He'll work them like slaves. I've already sent one of our lads there – Nigel Nobbs, d'you know him? He's a good, quiet lad and does whatever they want him to. We'll send young Wallace to join him. Nigel will be a good influence on the boy and the Hiltons will soon knock him into shape."

"Poor little devil. Oh well, I suppose it serves him right."

So Roger found himself in the headmaster's study. After a short lecture he bent over in the middle of the room and gripped his ankles while the headmaster caned him with the efficiency which comes of long practice. And then Roger was moved once more.

He was very upset. He had been happy with the Guthries and didn't want to move. They were upset too. They had never dreamed that the boy would be taken away from them. They felt that they had let him down and he felt that he had let them down. As a result they were all very miserable when he left and Mrs Guthrie had a good cry after he had gone.

# 26

# Broken China

The Hiltons lived in sheer luxury. Their house and garden were both large and beautiful, right across the other side of Beddingford on the outskirts of the town. They had a daughter Roger's age, a girl called Cynthia, and they had a three-year-old son Damien who was always in trouble.

Roger saw nothing of Jimmy now except at school and he never went out with the Quarry Gang again but Ledstock did single him out one day at school.

"Sorry to hear about your spot of bother young Wallace. But you kept your pledge to the gang and we're all proud of you for that."

For Roger, those few words from his hero balanced all the misery he had been through.

At the Hiltons he shared a large attic bedroom with Nigel. It had been the maids' room in the past. Nigel was a couple of years older than Roger, quiet, shy and a bit of a loner. But he and Roger got on well with one another. They always went to school together.

Their route took them past a hill with a bare rock face hidden behind a screen of bushes. It was about fifty yards back from the road. One afternoon Nigel took Roger behind the bushes to a small, shallow cave.

"If the Germans come this is going to be my hiding place," he said. "No one knows about it except us so you must keep it a secret."

"You bet," promised Roger. He had a new secret to replace that

144

of his secret gang.

Nigel added, "I keep digging out the back to make the cave bigger. I just spend a few minutes every day on my way home from school – not so long as to make me late though."

They were not to know that the danger of invasion had passed. The Germans had turned their attention to Russia and in doing so had sealed their fate. The bloodiest and most bitter battles of the war were to be fought in Russia and it was there more than anywhere else that the might of Germany was to be broken. But to the boys, invasion was still a vivid possibility.

"What a wizard idea," said Roger. "Can I help?"

"Of course you can. We'll make it big enough for both of us."

They didn't always leave school together in the afternoons. Roger often arrived at the cave first and worked at it until Nigel arrived. Yet somehow it never seemed to get much bigger.

When they got home from school they took off their shoes by the kitchen door and put on their slippers so as not to make the house dirty. They washed their hands at the kitchen sink and went in for tea. Nigel always made sure that they were home on time. He kept out of trouble if he possibly could.

Tea was a quiet affair. The boys only spoke if they were spoken to and Mrs Hilton rarely spoke to them. Such conversation as there was passed between the mother and her darling daughter Cynthia, with the addition of an occasional "Don't do that" thrown at Damien or "Mummy just look what Damien's doing" and more trouble for the boy.

Roger found himself taking sides with Damien and growing to dislike Cynthia more and more. But he enjoyed his tea for all that. Mrs Hilton made some very tasty oat cakes which made up for having to do without Mrs Guthrie's rock cakes.

After tea Mrs Hilton led her children from the room and Nigel and Roger cleared the table. Then they washed up. They took it in turns to wash and wipe. Nigel was very slow and careful. Roger tried but he had only been there a few days when he broke his first cup.

He cleared up the mess and then went through to the lounge and told Mrs Hilton. She came to the kitchen to look at the pieces in the bin. Cynthia came as well and gloated as Mrs Hilton went on and on about how precious the china was and how you couldn't replace it now it was war time.

g

After the washing up was done the two boys went to their bedroom. Nigel got on with his homework and Roger did the same. But he didn't have a lot to do, so he spent a lot of time reading. That night when Mr Hilton came home he was told all about the cup. He came up to the bedroom and gave Roger a thorough dressing down.

"All that fuss about one silly old cup," grumbled Roger after he had gone. "And it was only an ordinary cup. It's not as if they're short are they?"

"It was rather a nice cup," Nigel replied, "and Mrs Hilton's right. You can't get new ones now it's wartime."

"Oh don't you start," groused Roger. "And I hate that Cynthia. She really enjoyed them telling me off. And she's always being spiteful to little Damien. But I'll get her one of these days. You just see if I don't."

"Don't be silly. You want to steer clear of her," said Nigel seriously. "She's her mother's pet. You cross her and she'll get you in trouble with her mother and with her dad as well. Look at the way they treat Damien."

But Roger had made up his mind. When all four children were together he made a fuss of Damien and played with him and he was as nasty as he could be to Cynthia without actually getting into trouble. The nastier he was, the more she wanted him to like and admire her.

A few days later he dropped another cup. The Hiltons were furious and when he broke a third they went through the roof. Mr Hilton caned Roger for his carelessness and Mrs Hilton wrote to Roger's father – just to his father, not to both parents.

George didn't notice but when he passed the letter across to Lilian she noticed straight away and was angry. She was even more angry when she saw that Mrs Hilton had described Roger as 'a rather nasty little boy'. She told them that she was making a complaint to the school about him. It was clear that she was going to make things as difficult for their son as she could.

But George took her side.

"That boy always seems to be in trouble. He gets shifted from house to house. No one can put up with him for long. He's got a real chance with these Hiltons."

George was impressed by the thought that his son was living with a solicitor.

"I'd better go down for the weekend and sort him out. And I'll take some of our best china down to pacify the Hiltons."

"NO!" exploded Lilian. "That's the only decent china we've got. It was a wedding present."

"So it might have been, but I'm not having a boy of mine depriving decent people like the Hiltons."

"Decent people. Hm. They call Roger 'a nasty little boy'. That's our son they are talking about. I think that woman is a nasty piece of work."

George was shocked. He'd never heard his wife speak of anyone like that before. His exclamation showed his feelings.

"Lilian!"

"I'm sure it's true. There's our little boy been cut off from his home and all of us. It's no wonder if things go wrong sometimes."

"We've never had any of this trouble with Gerry or Margaret."

It was true. It always was Roger who was the one in trouble. They argued furiously but in the end Lilian gave way. She always did. But she wept as she wrapped up four cups, saucers and plates from her only set of decent china.

George travelled down alone that weekend. On the Saturday he went to see the Hiltons, apologised for his son and gave them his wife's treasured china. They were pleasantly surprised. He arranged to spend the Sunday with Roger and with Gerry and Margaret from their separate homes. But the rest of Saturday he spent with Roger alone.

First he lectured him. Then he caned him. Then he took him to the cinema as if nothing had happened. Roger felt it was all unfair but he felt pretty miserable when his father told him how upset his mother had been to lose her china.

Back at the Hiltons there were changes in the washing up arrangements. Nigel washed and wiped all the china and glass on his own. Then Roger took over and washed and wiped all the unbreakables. During the week that made life pretty easy for him because he only had the knives and spoons to do. But on Saturdays and Sundays he had all the saucepans and other cooking things. He was not pleased.

In fact he came to dislike the weekends more and more. On Saturday mornings, after they had done the breakfast washing up they went up to their room and cleaned it. Then they had to stand by their beds while Mrs Hilton inspected the room. Cynthia always came with her mother. Nigel didn't mind but Roger was infuriated.

"Snotty little bitch. I hate her."

"She's all right," said Nigel. "She can't help it if her mother spoils her."

On Saturday afternoons Mr Hilton took the children for a country walk. Roger usually had the sulks but found that he enjoyed the walks in spite of himself. He had a lot of fun chasing Damien and old man Hilton knew quite a lot about the country-side. He taught them to recognise some of the birds they saw, and the flowers and trees too, though Roger wasn't interested in those.

"Soft," he thought. He felt very differently when Mr Hilton found a slow worm, the first he had ever seen. All the children except Damien were a bit scared of this snake-like lizard, even though it was so small, but Mr Hilton picked it up and allowed each of them to stroke it and feel the beauty of its texture. Cynthia wouldn't. She was too squeamish and that pleased Roger. It gave him something to tease her about when they were on their own.

Sundays were the worst days of all. After the washing up the two boys went outside or out into the garage if it was raining. Mr Hilton had lined up all the shoes that had been used during the week together with their Sunday best – not that Nigel and Roger had a separate pair for Sunday. The two of them worked their way solidly through them all, cleaning and polishing until they were finished. Then Nigel fetched Mr Hilton to see that they had done a satisfactory job.

And by then it was time to go to the Parish Church. Roger wasn't used to the kind of service there. He didn't like all the psalms. They were boring and awkward to sing, not like hymns. Mr Hilton always read one of the lessons from the Bible. That was boring too. So were the sermons, even if they weren't as long as the ones in chapel. It was all boring. Boring, boring, boring.

And then there was all the Sunday washing up after dinner. Another family walk filled Sunday afternoon but Mrs Hilton came too and kept a firm check on Damien. So that was boring too. And then there was the tea washing up and off to the Parish Church again and after church they went straight home to supper and bed. There was only one word to describe it all thought Roger. He rather liked the word. Whenever adults wanted him to do something it was a word which always fitted perfectly. He used it a great deal. Everything was boring.

And yet strangely enough, on the whole Roger was reasonably happy and settled. For a while he managed to keep out of trouble although that was pure chance.

## 27

# Forbidden Fruit

The summer holidays came and Gerry left school. Soon he would be going home and finding a job.

"I don't see why we can't have them all home. There isn't much bombing any more," grumbled Lilian.

"Not much, but there's enough. You bring them home and you can guarantee that the next bomb will fall on us. Remember what happened to the Pollard's house when they brought Rachel home?"

Remember? She would never forget. The whole family wiped out.

"I suppose you're right," she sighed. She did so want her family to be together again.

"We could go down to Beddingford and have the three of them in a hotel with us for a couple of weeks. Then we can bring Gerry back home with us."

So down they went. They found a place in the village on the coast. They walked for miles, swam in the rock pool, went prawning and in the evenings Lilian played cards with the children while George puffed at his pipe and read. Gerry told Roger about a book called *Stalky and Co.* which was all about a school in that area.

"And if you enjoy *Stalky and Co.* you'll probably enjoy *Tom Brown's Schooldays* too."

So when the holiday was over and Roger was back with the Hiltons he went to the library and took out the two books.

"Smashing," he thought. "Why can't we have books like this

at school?"

Even Mrs Hilton couldn't keep an eye on the children all through the holiday. Roger began to get to know the girl who lived next door. She was about the same age as he was with unruly brown hair, a friendly freckled face and mischievous eyes. Roger asked Nigel about her.

"Oh her," said Nigel dismissively. "She goes to the same school as Cynthia. She's a bit nosy I think, always looking through the hedge."

"Perhaps she's bored. If she hasn't got anyone to play with she's bound to get bored isn't she. Why don't we ask her round?"

"We can't do that. You know Mrs Hilton doesn't want any of our friends here."

"She's not one of our friends is she. She's Cynthia's friend."

"No she's not. Cynthia's too snobby to be friends with her. Just because her dad's a solicitor she thinks she's too good for the likes of Jenny."

"Jenny. Is that what she's called? Well her dad must be pretty snobby for her to live in a house as good as this."

"I don't know what her dad is. I've never seen him."

Roger was standing in the front garden one day when he saw Jenny coming up the road. He slipped out into the road and walked towards her as if he was on his way to town.

"Hello Jenny," he said.

"Hello. How do you know my name?"

"I know all sorts of things," said Roger mysteriously.

"Silly fool. What's your name?"

"Roger Wallace."

"Well Roger Wallace why don't you walk with me past our two houses and down the lane."

"All right I will."

They walked down the lane to a barn on the edge of fields.

"You can kiss me if you like."

"I don't kiss girls."

"I'll bet you kiss that Cynthia Hilton then."

"No I don't."

"I bet you do."

"I don't. I think she's horrible."

"Well kiss me then, just to spite her."

So he kissed her clumsily and then felt awkward and silly.

151

"It's time I was home. I'll race you to the top of the lane," and she was off.

He raced after her. She was a good runner but he managed to catch her. At the top of the lane they stopped, breathless.

"I like you Roger Wallace," she said. "You're good fun." Then she kissed him again and was gone.

Poor Roger was smitten. For the next few days he was amazingly nice to Cynthia. She was surprised but she couldn't help being pleased. She wanted Roger to admire her. After all, he ought to admire her really.

She was especially pleased when he made one or two disparaging remarks about that 'freckle-faced girl next door.'

"That Jenny," she said. "Yes. Just because her dad's the captain of a ship she thinks she's something special."

Roger continued to be rude about Jenny until Cynthia thought it might be a good idea to invite her round just to point up the comparison between the two of them. She soon regretted it.

Jenny was a real tomboy. On the swing she went as high as either of the boys and if she showed her knickers what did she care. And she jumped off the swing just like a boy instead of demurely bringing it to a halt and slipping off gracefully as a girl should.

She played hide and seek with Damien and sometimes she and Roger hid together. He had no business hiding with her. Cynthia was jealous and angry. She felt that Roger had fooled her. He and Jenny fought and wrestled and played just like two boys – well not like Nigel. He was a nice boy. She soon decided not to have such an unpleasant girl in her garden ever again.

But it was too late. Roger and Jenny managed to spend a good deal of their holidays together. And when school began again he and Nigel found that they kept on seeing Jenny on the way to school. It was pure fluke of course but they started walking to school together. Even Nigel found that he liked this boisterous, lively girl. Before long he showed her his cave and she helped with the digging at the back of the cave, though the boys had rather lost interest in that.

After school she and Roger began to meet and walk back to the cave together.

"D'you want to see my titties?"

Roger was embarrassed but she pulled off her jumper.

To be truthful there wasn't much to see, just the faintest swelling, the promise of things to come. But Roger found himself fascinated and excited all the same. She shouldn't show herself to him like this and he shouldn't look.

"Go on, feel them," she said. "They're all soft."

He did as he was told. It was silly really. It was all nothing but he liked doing it. But he did feel confused and shy.

"Now let me see your thing."

"No," he said.

"Go on," she said. "It's only fair. You've seen my titties."

"No," he said. "It's not the same. It's . . . Well it's private."

"Oh don't be silly. You let me see your thing and I'll let you see my hole."

That finished him. He undid his fly buttons and they got to examining each other with a good deal of curiosity and pleasure.

The more Roger and Jenny saw of each other the more Cynthia hated them. And yet the more she hated Roger the more she wanted him to like her and the more she tried to please him.

October came and her daddy's precious apple trees at the bottom of the garden were bearing the very first crop of ripe apples. She offered one to Roger and one to Nigel. She even offered one to Damien.

"I don't think we should," said Nigel. "Your father has been looking forward to picking those apples."

"You don't need to worry about Daddy," she said. "He won't mind when he knows that I took them."

"Well I don't know," said Nigel doubtfully although he supposed she was probably right.

She took an apple from the nearest tree and bit into it. Then, like Eve of old, she persuaded them. Within a few days they had cleared that tiny first harvest completely.

Mr Hilton didn't notice his loss for several days. When he did notice he was furious. He told his wife to discover who was responsible. She called Cynthia to her and asked what had happened to the apples. Suddenly Cynthia felt frightened. She had never been in trouble with her parents before.

"It was that Roger," she said, "well and Damien but he can't reach on his own."

"What about Nigel?" asked Mrs Hilton.

"No it was just Roger and Damien," Cynthia answered. "I told them not to but they wouldn't listen. I said Daddy wanted to pick the apples himself at the proper time. But Roger wouldn't take any notice and of course Damien always does what Roger says."

So Mrs Hilton called Roger.

"Have you been picking and eating the apples in the garden?"

"Yes, Mrs Hilton."

"And have you given some to Damien?"

"Yes of course. He couldn't reach them for himself."

"So you have not only stolen our apples. You have been teaching our son to steal as well."

"We weren't stealing Mrs Hilton."

"Well what were you doing then?"

"We knew it was all right to have them because Cynthia offered them to us."

"What a wicked thing to say. Cynthia didn't offer them to you. She told you not to touch them."

"No she never. She picked them and gave them to us."

"Are you calling Cynthia a liar?"

"If she told you she didn't have any she is a liar."

"How dare you. Cynthia has never told me a lie in her life. She has told me exactly what happened so it's no use your pretending otherwise and telling me your lies."

"I'm not telling lies. It's your Cynthia who is telling lies."

Mrs Hilton looked as though she would explode.

"Go to your room this instant you dreadful child. Stay there until Mr Hilton comes home."

Roger was furious but there was nothing he could do. He went to the bedroom and stood staring moodily out of the window. When Nigel heard what had happened he went to Mrs Hilton and tried to tell her what really happened but she told him not to interfere.

"You keep out of this," she said. "It's nothing to do with you."

Nor would she allow him to go up to the bedroom to keep Roger company. But Roger had seen Jenny in her garden. He opened his window and told her what had happened. The two of them chattered on until Mr Hilton arrived home from work. Then Jenny waved and ran indoors and Roger closed his window and sat on his bed.

Mr Hilton had had a hard day. He was tired and irritable. No sooner was he inside the front door than his wife was telling him about the apples. He was angry about those apples. He was angry with his wife for bothering him about them before he had even got his coat off. Why couldn't the woman just let him inside the house and give him a while to sit down with a drink? He just wanted to be left in peace for a bit. But it was no use. She wouldn't leave it until he had seen the boy. That wretched boy. Nothing but trouble.

He climbed the stairs to the attic bedroom. Nigel tried to speak to him but Mr Hilton dismissed him with ease. He stepped into the bedroom and Roger got to his feet.

"So you are the apple thief."

"No Mr Hilton."

"Don't 'no' me. My wife has told me all about it. You will go to bed immediately and I shall deal with you in the morning. You will not go to school with Nigel tomorrow. You will come with me to my office and then I shall take you to school."

He stormed out of the bedroom and left Roger to go to bed.

As soon as he got downstairs he phoned Mr Wallace.

"I'm ringing about your boy. I'm afraid you are going to have to find somewhere else for him to live. My wife has had just about as much as she can stand what with his stealing and his lies."

George Wallace was appalled. He knew that Roger was often in trouble. But stealing and lies, this *was* something new.

"Stealing and lies Mr Hilton? Are you sure?"

"I'm a solicitor aren't I?" snapped Mr Hilton. "I don't make accusations lightly. The boy has stolen the whole of my apple crop and then tried to blame it all on my daughter."

Strangely enough George felt quite relieved. It was only a bit of scrumping after all. But he would have to go down and sort things out again. It was a real nuisance.

Wearily he said, "I'll catch the train down tomorrow evening and take the boy from you on Saturday morning if that is all right."

"Yes Mr Wallace, that will be fine. Thank you."

George Wallace joined his wife and Gerry and told them about the call.

"I don't know what we are going to do with the boy," he said.

"We could always bring him home," said Lilian hopefully.

"You know I won't have that," answered George. "The school

155

will have to sort something out for us."

"Why don't you ask Miss Holly?" said Gerry. "She looked after me pretty well and she hasn't got anyone in my place."

"That's a good idea," said Lilian. "You go and phone her George straight away."

"She's not on the phone," Gerry reminded her.

"Then we'll all go down tomorrow night and while you fetch Roger from the Hiltons, we'll go and see Miss Holly."

So another journey to Beddingford was arranged rather sooner than they had expected.

# 28

# Punishments, Truth and Lies

The following morning Mr Hilton took Roger with him to his office and told him to wait in the waiting room.

At about a quarter past nine a middle-aged woman called Roger to come into the office as if he were one of Mr Hilton's clients. The office was a gloomy sort of room. Everything was dull, dark brown and dusty. There were great piles of papers and files everywhere and there was a bookcase full of huge old books. It was utterly depressing. Mr Hilton was sitting behind a dark, heavy desk.

"I'm just going to phone your headmaster," he said. "Perhaps you would like to listen to our conversation."

He phoned the school and was put through to the headmaster.

"Ah, headmaster, I'm afraid that Roger Wallace is not at school yet. I have kept him with me and will bring him to school myself."

"Nothing wrong I hope," said the headmaster.

"Yes there certainly is something wrong. We have a small orchard at home which was bearing its first crop this year. The Wallace boy has not only stolen the apples; he has also lied to my wife and tried to put the blame on my daughter. As you know, he was sent to us because he was a trouble-maker in need of a firm hand. We have done our best with him but he certainly needs to be disciplined over this matter."

The headmaster quite understood and promised that he would attend to it. The phone call ended. Roger was angry and bitter. They called him a liar but they were the liars.

"Now," said Mr Hilton taking up his walking stick, "bend over that chair."

Roger stood still. "I didn't steal the apples," he said.

"Don't make me even more angry than I am already," answered Mr Hilton. "Bend over that chair."

It was no use arguing. Roger gritted his teeth and bent over the chair. Four times the walking stick came down on his backside and each stroke was harder than the last but Roger never made a sound. He stood up when the caning was over and glared white-faced at Mr Hilton. Mr Hilton looked away. Could the boy be right after all? Impossible.

"Come with me," he said and took Roger to school where he handed him over to the headmaster.

Up to this moment Roger had just been angry and bitter but in the headmaster's study he began to feel scared as well. And he desperately needed to go to the toilet. After Mr Hilton had gone the headmaster turned to him and said, "Well boy, what have you got to say for yourself?"

"Sir, I didn't steal the apples and I didn't tell lies."

"Don't make things worse boy. Mr Hilton is a highly respected member of this community. He is also a lawyer. He wouldn't tell me that you have been a liar and a thief unless it were true."

"But sir . . . "

"Don't interrupt boy. You're a disgrace to the school. And I believe that you are also a wolf cub. You are a disgrace to the Scouting movement. As from now you are expelled from the cubs. Do you understand?"

"Yes sir."

"I am not going to expel you from the school even though you have let us down so badly. You have also let your parents down, as if they hadn't enough to worry about with bombs falling all round them every night. Goodness knows what your father must think of you. He's coming down tonight so we shall soon know."

"But sir," Roger tried again desperately but it was no use.

"Silence. Do you think I want to listen to more of your lies? Now, bend down where you are and take hold of your shins."

Roger urgently needed the toilet but he did as he was told. The first stroke of the headmaster's cane finished him. He couldn't hold his water any longer. It poured down his leg, down his sock and over his shoe onto the carpet. Roger was horrified - terrified.

Now he really was for it. He was so busy watching the patch on the carpet grow that the other five strokes of the cane were almost an irrelevance. He felt so ashamed. Not because of the apples. He knew he hadn't done anything wrong about those. But he was ashamed that he had wet himself and he was very scared. But the headmaster never noticed. He strode back to his desk.

"Now. Stand up boy and go to your class. Let's have no more nonsense from you in the future."

"Yes sir," gasped Roger.

"Not just 'yes sir' boy. 'Thank you sir' is also required."

"Yes sir. Thank you sir." For goodness sake. He wanted to get out of there.

"Very well. Now report to your class teacher."

Roger did his best to walk out of the study as if nothing had happened. He went straight to the washrooms, tried to clean himself up, and then went to his class.

By the time of the mid-morning break everyone in the class knew what had happened. They all wanted to see his bum, so a crowd of them went to the school lavatories.

"Cor."

"Wow."

"It's going blue and yellow already."

Roger felt better just listening to them. He had taken a fair old walloping twice without ever crying out. And his pals listened to his story and believed it, especially when Nigel backed him up.

Jenny had heard all about things from Nigel on the way to school. By the end of lunch-time she had discovered the rest of the story and had spread it about her own school. Cynthia was not very popular at the best of times. Now they put her in Coventry. Everywhere she went at school all the other girls cut her dead. She went home crying and told her mother, "That Roger has been spreading his lies all through my school."

"Don't give him another thought dear. He will be leaving us tomorrow and he'll be confined to his room until then. Just remember 'sticks and stones may break your bones but words can never hurt you'."

Cynthia knew the old saying. For the first time in her life she realised that it was rubbish. Why wasn't she popular like that Jenny next door. She was much cleverer and much, much more beautiful.

Meanwhile Roger and Jenny had walked home together. She asked him all about what had happened and then she led him to the cave.

"I want to see your bum," she said.

He and Jenny were well past all shyness and by now he was beginning to feel quite proud of his bum.

"Gosh," she said. "You've got some whopping bruises. I'm glad they don't cane girls like that."

He pulled up his shorts and they chatted until Nigel arrived, and then the three of them went home. Mrs Hilton greeted them at the kitchen door. She said to Roger, "You, go straight to your room and pack your things. You will stay there until your father comes in the morning. And you can go without tea or supper.

"Nigel, go and sit up to tea."

They both did as they were told, but Nigel was amazed that Mrs Hilton was so hard. As he cleared the table after tea, he collected some of the left overs and slipped up to the bedroom to make sure that Roger didn't go hungry. It was the first time in his life that he had stepped out of line and he felt very daring.

Roger ate the tea Nigel had brought him and then began to pack his belongings. He would be glad to get out of this place. They were all rotten, all except Damien. He was all right.

He had almost come to the end of his packing when he had his brainwave. He knew how he would get back at them. And it would be nice for his mum too. But how could he do it and get away with it? He had never thought about anything so carefully in his life before. At last he knew exactly what he was going to do. If only he could stay awake.

He sat at the top of the attic stairs and listened as Damien was put to bed. After a while he heard Cynthia and Nigel saying their goodnights and he went back into the room. He took his slippers off and got into bed with all his clothes on.

Nigel came and got ready for bed and the two of them chatted for a while. Nigel fell asleep and Roger was finding it very difficult not to do the same. He got up, put his slippers and dressing gown on and sat at the top of the stairs again. He slept and woke with a jerk feeling cold and uncomfortable. The Hiltons were going to bed.

He slipped back into his bed but this time he was wide awake. The Hiltons seemed to take ages before they were quiet. He crept out to the top of the stairs. All the lights downstairs had been switched off. He left his slippers behind and crept downstairs on his bare feet. Why did everything creak so loud?

He went outside and fetched a box and some newspapers from the garden shed. He took them into the dining-room. From the sideboard he carefully removed four cups, saucers and plates. He wrapped them in newspaper and put them in the box. Then he went out to the kitchen, put his shoes on and slipped out of the house with the box.

He made his way to the cave and placed the box at the very back. He covered it over with some of the slatey rock and then covered it all over with dead leaves.

"There," he said to himself, "they won't notice until Sunday and by then it will be too late. And they'll never think to look in there 'cos no one knows about the cave except Nigel and Jenny. One day my mum can have her best china back again. So there."

With immense satisfaction he made his way back to the house and up to his bed. He had good reason to be pleased. No one had seen him. He slept like a top and the following morning his father arrived early and collected him.

To everyone's embarrassment Roger ran into his father's arms and clung to him. George felt quite moved but it was a bit awkward with the Hiltons there. He was as glad as his son to get away from that house. But as they walked away he felt just as awkward with his son. What on earth should he say to the boy? How should he behave? He couldn't just pretend that it was all over. So they walked more or less in silence until they came to the hotel on the river-front and Roger was reunited with his mother and with Gerry and Margaret.

Once again he ran into his mother's arms but this time the flood gates opened. He clung to her and wept. Margaret wondered what on earth had got into him. His mother held him tight.

"If only George would let the children come home," she thought, "but it's no use. He won't and that's that."

Slowly Roger became aware that there was someone else in the room, a stranger. He wiped his eyes and stood back from his mother. Gerry sensed the awkwardness and stepped in.

"Roger, I would like you to meet Miss Holly. She used to look after me when I was in Beddingford."

Gerry suddenly seemed so grown up now he had left school.

161

And he was taller too. Roger shook Miss Holly by the hand and looked at her with a good deal of curiosity. She wasn't much bigger than he was.

She said, "Your parents have told me that you need a home to live in."

"Yes Miss."

"Now that Gerry has gone home I've got a room to spare."

She looked at him. He didn't know whether he was supposed to say anything so he just waited. She turned to his parents.

"I must be getting along soon. I look after my nephew's shop on a Saturday. Could I just have a little chat with Roger on his own do you think?"

They weren't at all sure. Come to that, they weren't at all sure about anything. Again Gerry stepped in.

"I'll take you to our bedroom. You can have a chat with him there."

He left them and the two of them sat side by side on his bed. She said, "Gerry's a nice young man isn't he."

"Yes Miss Holly."

"I liked looking after him. Now, I hear you've been in a bit of trouble.'

"Yes Miss."

"Well dear, I've heard what people say but I don't know that I've heard the truth yet. If you don't mind I would like you to tell me the whole story. But make sure you tell me nothing but the truth mind."

So Roger told her simply and truthfully. The more she listened the more angry she became. When he had finished she said very quietly, "And that is the truth?"

"Yes Miss," Roger replied simply.

She put her arm round his shoulders and said, "I believe you Roger but you do understand that there will be a lot of people who won't, don't you?"

"Yes Miss." And the tears streamed down his face because she believed him.

She handed him a handkerchief and said, "Well now, you've got a big decision to make. Will you come and live with me and take your brother's old room?"

"Yes please Miss Holly," he sniffled.

"That's all right then. Cheer up boy. Everything's going to be all right."

She gave him a big hug and took him back to his parents. He was sent off to join the other two children and Miss Holly said, "He has told me his story and I'm sure he's told me the truth. I think he has been very unfairly treated. But there's no use crying over spilt milk is there. I'll be very glad to have him if that's all right by you."

They were so relieved. And Lilian felt sure that Miss Holly was right. She believed in her boy. He might be mischievous but he wasn't a bad boy. She was sure of it.

George was not so sure. He wondered if Miss Holly had had the wool pulled over her eyes. Mr Hilton was a solicitor and George was rather overawed by solicitors. And then there was the headmaster. He had backed up Mr Hilton. George was rather overawed by headmasters too. Miss Holly had probably let her affection for Gerry lead her astray. He was thankful she would take Roger, but he must do something about the boy. He felt that his son was at some sort of crossroads. But how to tackle it, that was the question.

Miss Holly was speaking again. "You'll have a lot to do this weekend and you'll want to enjoy your children. Why don't you come to me for a meal after chapel tomorrow evening. You can leave in time to catch your train and I'll see little Margaret safely to her home."

She went her way with their gratitude ringing in her ears. Roger's future was settled once more, but his ordeal was not yet over.

# 29

# Ruffled Feathers

That afternoon they all went for a walk over the hills to the sea. George was still struggling within himself. The boy had been caned twice. Wasn't that enough? Should he just drop the subject?

No he didn't think he could do that. His son must be made to see how serious things were. Perhaps he should try some of this new psychology stuff. He chose a moment when his wife was talking to Margaret.

"You stay with them," he said to Gerry. "I want a word with Roger."

Taking Roger with him, he began to stride ahead until the others were left well behind and then he started.

"You know that I have had telephone conversations with both Mr Hilton and your headmaster?"

Oh, not that old business all over again. "Yes Dad."

"I know that they may not have got things altogether right, but there's no smoke without a fire is there. And you do seem to be in trouble pretty often."

That was true so Roger said nothing. He was just fed up with the whole thing. Why couldn't his dad leave it alone? He'd already been caned and kicked out of the Hilton's house – not that he minded that. "Good riddance to bad rubbish" was what he thought of them. And then he giggled. "I expect that's what they think of me too," he thought.

His father was blissfully unaware that Roger wasn't listening to a word he said. He went on and on. But at last something clicked and Roger was listening again.

"I'm afraid we must have been very poor parents. We must have brought you up very badly for you to have become such a nuisance of a boy. We have let you down."

"No," said Roger. He was confused. His dad shouldn't say such things. He felt he had the best parents in the world. He loved them and was proud of them and respected them. It wasn't their fault if he got into trouble sometimes – not just this time when he shouldn't have been in trouble, but other times. He wanted to protest but he didn't know how.

His father misunderstood completely. He felt rather pleased with himself. He had obviously made an impact. He had got to the boy and made him feel ashamed of himself. This psychology stuff really worked. If he could just drive his lesson home he might help his boy to make a new start. He picked up a stick from the hedge and cleared it of leaves and twigs.

"You've been such a bad boy," he said, "because I have been such a bad father to you. So it's not you who should be caned. It's me. I think perhaps you had better punish me and then we can put this whole nasty business behind us."

Roger was appalled. It wasn't right. He couldn't do it. He wouldn't do it.

But his father made him take the stick. Then he stood behind Roger and placed one hand over the hand that held the stick. He held out his other hand and made Roger cane him. Roger felt that his heart would break. He sobbed and sobbed.

His father misunderstood the tears completely. He felt that he had got it right. Roger was now truly sorry for what he had done and there was a good chance that he would turn over a new leaf.

Roger himself couldn't have put into words why he was crying. But mostly it was because he had told the truth and his father had not believed him. He knew that his father was trying to act for the best and for his good. And he would always love his father. But their relationship would never be quite the same again. His father had neither listened to him nor trusted him. From that moment there came the first beginnings of an awareness that he would have to stand on his own feet in life. If his father didn't trust him, how could he trust his father?

The walk continued but there was no joy in it. He took the first opportunity to get away from his dad and back to Gerry and Margaret.

They spent the evening at the hotel playing cards with their mother. She enjoyed that as much as they did. George sat contentedly reading and smoking his pipe, blissfully unaware of the damage he had done.

On Sunday morning they all went to chapel. During the sermon Roger leaned against his mother and felt warm and comfortable. She put her hand on his knee and stroked it gently. He felt soothed and happy.

After chapel George had a brief word with Roger's headmaster and arranged to call on him late that afternoon. The Head had a few words with Gerry. He was pleased to see that at least one member of the family was turning out well. The school did a good job, he thought.

They walked back to the hotel, had a skimpy lunch and then went for another walk to the sea. When they arrived back it was time for George to go and see the headmaster.

"I'll see you all at chapel," he said.

He had no sooner gone than Mr Hilton exploded onto the scene. He had come straight from home, had positively rushed. He was hot and sticky and furiously angry. But he was confronted by Lilian. He wasn't very good with women. It was a set-back. He felt her coldness as she greeted him.

"Mr Hilton?"

"Good afternoon Mrs Wallace. I . . . " How on earth should he tell her? "Things have gone beyond a joke. Not content with all he has done your boy has stolen some of our best china."

Suddenly he felt very awkward. He could hardly tell her that it was only her china that had gone missing. He had always felt that his wife had made too much fuss over that china. But it really was too bad.

Lilian bristled. "Oh come now. What would a little boy want with china?"

"I've no idea. I don't pretend to understand your son one bit. But the china was there last Sunday and now it has gone. No one else could have taken it."

"I'll go and fetch Roger," she said.

She fetched him and said, "As you can see, Mr Hilton has come to see me. He says that you have stolen their best china. Is that true?"

"No Mother."

"Oh come now," exploded Mr Hilton. "Don't you think I've heard enough of your lies boy."

Roger flared. "I've told you no lies. It's your . . . "

"Roger!" His mother silenced him and then she turned back to Mr Hilton. With icy tones she said, "I'll deal with this if you don't mind Mr Hilton. I don't need to remind you that my son is no longer in your care." She turned back to Roger. "Now Roger, let me ask you again. I want the truth mind, no matter how bad it may be. Have you stolen Mr and Mrs Hilton's china?"

"No mother." He looked her straight in the eye.

"You realise that it will be very easy for me to check whether you are telling me the truth?"

"Yes Mother."

"And you still say that you did not steal their china."

"Yes Mother." He felt completely calm and unafraid. He looked straight at her. He had not stolen their china. He had just taken her china back again. One day she would be pleased. It wasn't the Hilton's china. He was telling the truth.

She turned back to Mr Hilton who had watched the whole thing amazed. What a bare-faced liar the boy was. How brazen.

"Do you know when the china was stolen Mr Hilton?"

"Not exactly, no, but it was some time . . . "

"Yes you said, some time after last Sunday. Did anybody see Roger steal the china?"

"Well, no, but who else . . . "

"You are making very serious accusations Mr Hilton. In fact they are rather dangerous accusations for a solicitor to make don't you think? You'd better come with me and search the boy's room."

Mr Hilton was feeling more and more uncomfortable. And yet it must be the boy. No one else would have chosen those four cups, saucers and plates and nothing else. It must be the boy.

He went with Mrs Wallace to Roger's room and they searched but found nothing. Roger had been sent back to Gerry and Margaret.

"We'd better go and search Margaret's room. Such an accomplished criminal might have thought that we would search here," she said sarcastically.

"Oh no I . . . "

"Oh yes. I insist."

Again they searched and found nothing.

"Now my own room Mr Hilton."

"I really don't think that will be necessary."

"Of course it is necessary," she snapped.

She turned out drawers, the wardrobe, their cases. She made him look under the bed and on top of the wardrobe. He was feeling terrible. What a harridan the woman was.

"There Mr Hilton. Shall we call the police and ask them to investigate this crime?"

"I . . . I think that perhaps we have made a terrible mistake." Yet he couldn't think that they had. He didn't know what to think. "Perhaps the events of the past few weeks have affected our judgement somewhat."

"Perhaps the events of the past few weeks are not quite as you and your wife have portrayed them Mr Hilton."

This angry little woman made him squirm. He apologised profusely and left as quickly as he could. But what on earth was he to say to his wife?

"You see my dear, there was no proof. And you know how dangerous it is to make accusations if you can't prove them. That Mrs Wallace is a dreadful woman, but you don't need to worry. Her husband will give the boy what for."

"That won't bring my china back," his wife snapped.

"No. No that's true, but at least we shall have nothing in the house to remember that awful family by."

Meanwhile Lilian decided to say nothing to George or to anyone else come to that. It was certainly strange. She wondered about young Roger. But he had been through enough recently without any more fuss. 'Least said soonest mended', she thought. "Let's hope Miss Holly will have no trouble."

# 30

# At Home With Miss Holly

That Sunday evening they all went to chapel. During the sermon Roger leaned against his mother again. And again she put her hand on his knee and kneaded it gently with her thumb. He felt soothed and happy and so did she. He was a good . . . no, a dear boy, this youngest son of hers. After chapel they walked down the hill into the High Street until they came to Miss Holly's cottage. It was tiny. The Hilton's house had been the biggest Roger had ever lived in. This one was the smallest.

The cottage was one of a terrace with the front door opening onto the pavement. So as Miss Holly opened the door to them they stepped straight from the pavement into her dark little front room. Even with the gas lamps lit the room was still very dark. But there was a cheerful coal fire burning in the fireplace, and if the little old lady looked a bit like a whiskery witch it was obvious that she was a nice witch.

She welcomed them into her home and showed them around. There wasn't a lot to see. The front room was the only living room. Behind it there was a tiny kitchen with a cooker and a sink with a cold water tap. Outside was a tiny yard with a meat safe on one side and the toilet on the other. The stairs went up from the corner of the front room in a spiral. Eight stairs up led to the back bedroom which had a double bed in and almost no room for anything else except the wardrobe and dressing table. That was Miss Holly's room. Two more steps up led to the front bedroom which also had a double bed in it and wardrobe and dressing table. If anything it was even smaller than Miss Holly's room.

169

h

"This used to be my room," said Gerry as they all crowded in.

"And now 'tis gwain to be your brother's," added Miss Holly. "Do you think you'll be comfy my dear?"

Roger felt rather proud that he was to have Gerry's old room. "Oh yes," he said. "It will be fine."

They went down to the living room and when they were all sitting around the table there was barely room to move. Miss Holly bustled about bringing in dishes of vegetables and last of all, a huge rabbit pie. And all the time she chattered away.

"The vegetables is from my nephew's garden. And one of my varmer friends brought the rabbits into the shop vor me. It do help out with the rations when ee can get zummat extra don't it."

She served out the pie and asked them to help themselves to vegetables.

"There now. Is that enough for ee Mr Wallace? And you missus? And how about you Gerry. My how tall you be now. Come on, eat up. You got a long way to go on that train tonight. All the way past Lunnon. Oh my dear soul. And how about you my dears?" (to Roger and Margaret). "There's plenty here. Have a bit more pie. Do ee like the crust boy? You'm gwain to be my favourite boy id'n' you."

So it went on non stop. Stewed apples and thick clotted cream followed. They ate until they could eat no more. Then the leaves of the table were dropped and it was pushed back against the wall so that they could all sit round the fire – all except Roger and Margaret who played games on the table.

The adults sat chatting until it was time for farewells. The Wallaces took Margaret back to her home before crossing the bridge to the station. Roger was on his own once more with no one but Miss Holly for company. She didn't let him brood.

"Let's have a game or two of draughts shall us?"

They played until supper time. The house was lit by gas. Somehow that made them feel drowsy earlier than they would have done with electric light. The lamps fizzed away and contributed to the general feeling of cosiness.

"Shall us have some zupper dear?"

"Supper. Oh gosh, I couldn't eat any more," Roger said.

"Aw git on with ee. A big boy like you can always eat."

"No really. I'm still full up with rabbit pie."

"Well I wouldn't have believed it. I'll just go and make some coo coo then."

Roger wondered what on earth 'coo coo' was until she came in with two mugs of cocoa. They sat quietly by the fire drinking up and then Roger got ready for bed.

He climbed up the short winding staircase carrying his candle carefully so that it didn't blow out. He undressed and opened the curtains a little so that light shone into the room from the moon. Then he snuffed out the candle and got into bed.

He was just dozing off when something landed with a plonk on the bed.

He was petrified.

Whatever it was, it began to move across the bed. He wanted to shout for help but his voice wouldn't come. He couldn't breathe. And then he heard it and all his fears disappeared. It was Pusser the cat and he was purring.

Roger stretched out his hand and felt his warm, soft fur. He stroked him and then he was asleep.

When Miss Holly went to bed, she crept up the extra stairs with her candle and peeped in at him lying fast asleep with the cat curled up on his bed. Quietly she placed his arm beneath the bedclothes.

"The dear of him," she whispered to herself. "He seems a nice enough boy to me. Well Miss Holly, I'll tell ee what. He'll be a danged vine boy afore you've finished with un."

And with that she said her prayers, climbed into her big double bed and slept the sleep of a child.

She had Roger up in good time in the morning and sent him off to school. He met Jenny after school and walked part of the way home with her. She wanted to know everything that had happened to him. Without saying anything they both knew that their friendship had run its course. Jenny wasn't worried. She had enjoyed Roger but there were plenty of other friends about.

In fact, their friendship stopped at once. Jimmy Smith called for Roger on his way to school that Tuesday. His route to school took him right past Roger's front door. The two boys had remained pals at school and were now able to spend leisure time together again.

When they arrived at Roger's on their way home, they both went indoors. The tiny front room became a battle ground of model soldiers, cowboys and Indians and artillery that would

171

actually fire matchsticks across the mat.

As soon as they arrived home Miss Holly asked, "Would you like a drop of herb beer boys?

She was a strict teetotaller so of course it was non-alcoholic and yet it gave the boys a nice burning sensation as it went down their throats. And every so often there would be a loud explosion in the kitchen as one of the bottles burst spraying herb beer all over the kitchen ceiling. For a non-alcoholic drink it seemed to pack quite a punch.

"Tastes just like the stuff old Sam used to give us," said Jimmy.

"Old Sam dear?" queried Miss Holly.

"He was a friend we used to have before the war. He worked for my dad a bit," said Roger.

"Lived out in the wood in a large shed," added Jimmy. "He taught us fishing and catching rabbits and things."

"Did he dear?" said Miss Holly. She was not at all sure about this friend of theirs. Sounded a bit like a poacher to her. She was surprised that Mr Wallace should have employed such a man. But there, it was not for her to judge. "Judge not, that ye be not judged," she said to herself.

That first week slipped by and in no time it was Friday night and bath night. After tea Miss Holly put a screen across the living room and placed a zinc tub in front of the fire. She poured in kettle after kettle of steaming hot water and then left Roger to get on with his bath.

He fitted into the tub just about perfectly. It was pleasant lying there in the hot water watching the flames flickering in the fire and dreaming. Miss Holly let him lie there for a while and then she called, "Come on boy. Don' ee let thick water get cold."

He dragged himself back into the real world, washed himself, towelled himself down and put on his pyjamas.

Together they took the tub out into the yard and emptied it. Miss Holly gave it a good scrub round and put it away. Then the two of them played ludo until it was time for supper.

Supper was a great hunk of home made bread plastered with thick clotted cream and a further rich coating of home made jam. It was rounded off with the inevitable mug of coo-coo.

On Saturday morning Miss Holly had Roger out of bed just as early as on a school day. She busied herself around and then the two of them set off for the shop. Her nephew owned a hardware shop. There never seemed to be much stock or many customers but Roger enjoyed serving the few people who did come in. His mental arithmetic improved no end.

At lunch-time Miss Holly shut the shop and the two of them went down into the basement. It was the stock room but there was a small kitchen down there. Miss Holly cooked bacon, egg, tomatoes, fried bread, chips and anything else she could lay her hands on and the two had their meal on the spot. Then she said, "Now boy, you've done very well this morning. You'd better take the afternoon off. Make sure you'm home well before dark won't ee."

He promised and made his escape. He was free. He hadn't realised how much he needed to be free. Miss Holly was all right. He liked her. And he liked living at her house. But she was a bit smothering. Every minute with her she was either talking to him or playing with him. She hardly ever left him on his own – except when Jimmy was there. She did leave the two of them to play on their own.

Now he was properly on his own and it was important that he was. He had things to do. First he went home. He emptied his school satchel and put a couple of old newspapers in it. He put his gas mask in the wardrobe, but carried the gas mask case over his shoulder. And then he set off.

He walked towards the Hiltons until he came to the cave. Checking that there was nobody about he slipped behind the hedge into the cave. At the back he found his mother's china untouched. He didn't think anybody had been there since he had. He took the china, wrapped it again and put it in his gas-mask case and his satchel.

Then he set off for the coast. At first he was quite apprehensive, half expecting someone to clap him on the shoulder and ask, "What have you got in that satchel then?" But as he left the town behind and climbed over the hills his fears melted away and he began to enjoy himself. He came down to the cliffs and walked along the bracken fringed path to the old coastguard station. There, in a corner, he emptied out the china and stacked it carefully away. He covered it with bracken and then with stones until it was completely hidden from view. Then he altered the arrangement of their log seats so that it would be a corner that was neither noticed nor used. When he was finally satisfied, he set off

173

for home.

"There," he said to himself. "When the war's over I'll come and get that and take it home to Mum. She'll be pleased to get it back again I expect."

The weeks and months slipped by. Most Saturday afternoons he either spent with Jimmy or on his own. They sometimes went to the cattle market but usually they just mucked about down by the river. There was always something to do and they never got bored.

The Japanese attacked Pearl Harbour and so, at long last, the Americans entered the war. And then it was Christmas again – Christmas 1941.

By a lucky chance Roger's whole family was free at the same time. They were not to know it at the time, but it was to be their very last Christmas as a complete family. Mr and Mrs Wallace took rooms at the hotel on the riverside and Miss Holly invited them all to have their Christmas dinner at her cottage.

They all went to the Christmas morning service at the chapel on the hill. As they climbed the hill, Mr Wallace led the way on his own. Lilian followed with Alfie and Eric, both of them in their RAF uniforms.

Alfie was a navigator with bomber command. He had already flown over Germany a bit. Some of his friends had been shot down and others wounded. He was more subdued than anyone had ever seen him, not that Roger or Margaret noticed.

Eric was still in training as a fighter pilot. Destined for a hurricane squadron when he had achieved his wings, he would argue with anybody that the hurricane was a better plane than a spitfire. He couldn't wait to be in action.

Gerry brought up the rear with Roger and Margaret, amused to see Roger so proud of his RAF brothers. It would not be long before he would be in uniform too. He was going into the army. He wondered if Roger would be as proud of him in an army uniform as he was of the other two in the RAF. If he realised how scared it all made him, he wouldn't be so proud.

After chapel, they made their way to Miss Holly's cottage and all crowded into the tiny front room. There was no space anywhere. The table was fully out. Miss Holly had borrowed extra chairs from the chapel and there was nothing for it but just to get in somehow and sit down.

"Take their coats up to your room Roger, there's a good lad," said Miss Holly.

Golly, those RAF greatcoats weren't half heavy. He got them upstairs and plonked them all down on his bed. Pusser was already there keeping well out of the way. He gave him a stroke and then rejoined the family. What a squash. There wouldn't be any room to raise their elbows when they ate so he wouldn't be ticked off for not keeping them close to his sides. Not that anyone would notice. It was too dark.

Miss Holly and Mr Wallace bustled to and fro with the vegetable dishes and then a great cheer went up as Miss Holly struggled in with a large Christmas goose. She had got it off the ration from one of her farmer friends.

"You carve Mr Wallace while I go and see to the gravy."

He began to carve and then whispered, "There doesn't seem to be much meat on this bird except on the legs. Don't say anything to upset her."

Carefully he shared out small portions of meat for everyone and they all helped themselves to vegetables. He carried the carcase out into the kitchen. Moments later he was back again, still carrying the carcase and roaring with laughter.

"I think you should have put the lights on Miss Holly," he said. "I've been carving off the back of the bird. Would anybody like a slice or two of breast?"

And so the plates were piled high and emptied and Christmas pudding followed. Miss Holly and Mrs Wallace sent the family packing while they cleared away.

It was a cool, crisp afternoon and they walked the hills to the sea and back in time for Christmas tea. Boxing Day was spent walking too. Miss Holly had made a mountain of sandwiches and the family set off for the coast once more.

Although there were areas where they had to detour because of barbed wire and mines, most of the coast path was still open. George strode ahead, swinging his walking stick and revelling in the winter sunshine and the fresh, pure air. It was so good to be far from the sound of bombs and the thought of war. It was right to have Roger and Margaret down here.

Ten yards behind the two boys in uniform walked either side of their mother, enjoying each other's company and making her feel very proud. And way back, Gerry kept Roger and Margaret entertained with a series of stories and games so that they were unaware of just how far their father was taking them.

They sat on the cliffs and ate their lunches. George shared his tobacco pouch with Eric and the two of them puffed away at their pipes. And then the whole family had a mad game of hide and seek in the bracken, taking it in turns to seek. Even Mr and Mrs Wallace joined in.

But when it was time to go home it dawned on them that none of them had seen Margaret for ages. They called and whistled but there was no reply. So then they stretched out in a line and began to search. Their feet crunched and crackled as they trampled over the dead bracken side by side.

They worked their way from one end of the headland to the other and back again. Then they moved further to one side and began again, whistling and calling all the time. They tried a third time and this time, at last, they found her sitting in the middle of a clump of bushes beautifully hidden from sight.

"Why didn't you come when we called and whistled?"

"I was hiding," she answered.

There was no arguing with that.

The journey home seemed to take for ever and Roger and Margaret grew more and more tired and crotchety but at last they arrived back at Miss Holly's.

Hunks of home-made bread and jam and mince pies, both of them smothered in cream and followed by Christmas cake, filled every last corner. And then it was time for Roger and Margaret to go to bed. Margaret shared Roger's bed that night.

Suddenly it was all over. Alfie and Eric went back to their RAF stations, Gerry and his parents went home and Margaret went back to her evacuee home. Roger was left alone with Miss Holly and Pusser. It seemed very quiet with all the family gone.

Roger didn't often feel lonely. He was used to being on his own. But he felt lonely then. Two days wasn't enough. He hardly seemed to have seen Alfie and Eric at all. He fingered the coin in his pocket. Alfie had given it to him. A whole shilling. Wowee.

# 31

# The Skimmington

The new year began and Roger and Margaret went back to school. It was 1942. Roger was happy and comfortable with Miss Holly and although he wasn't doing particularly well at school, he was keeping out of trouble.

Easter came and with it the holidays. One day as Roger was wandering by the river he saw Barbara getting into a rowing boat, helped in by one of the fishermen Roger knew. He ran alongside and said, "Where are you going? Can I come?"

Barbara was looking rather serious and pale. She said, "No Roger, I don't think you'd better come."

"Why not? I can help row."

"No. I don't think you should."

"Let'n come," said the fisherman. "As long as 'ee stays with me he won't come to no 'arm."

Barbara still demurred. "It isn't right. He shouldn't be there."

"Oh git on. 'Ee won't understand what 'tis all about. Come on boy. You take the oars in the bow."

So Roger jumped in and soon he and the fisherman were rowing steadily downstream against the tide. It was hard work and they made slow progress. Barbara sat stiff and silent in the stern. Roger had never seen her look so serious. As they drew near to a village called Opstow-water a strange noise began. Barbara urged them to hurry and the colour drained from her face. Roger wondered what on earth was the matter. Opposite Opstow's main street they drew alongside the quay steps and Barbara jumped out. "You stay where you are in the boat," she

177

said to Roger and then she began to hurry up the street. Her great mane of ginger hair was swept high up from her forehead. She seemed incredibly tall as she strode towards the noise – and it really was a noise now. They had never heard anything like it. Around the top of the street came a young woman carrying two suitcases and behind her there was a great crowd of women all screaming and shouting and banging on saucepans and frying pans and making the most terrible racket. At the head of the crowd a large, fat women was carrying an effigy on a long stick. It looked a bit like a statue of Jesus or the Virgin Mary or Guy Fawkes. As they drew closer Roger saw that it was the model of a woman with a hangman's noose around her neck. He didn't realise that it was supposed to look like the woman with the suitcases. All he saw was Barbara striding straight towards the crowd. He felt frightened for her.

"What's going on?" he asked.

The fisherman answered, "Tid'n none of our business boy. Never you mind what 'tis all about. 'Tis women's business."

Roger looked at Barbara again and then jumped out of the boat and ran after her.

"Yer boy. Come back. Don' ee go getting mixed up in all that."

But he was too late. Roger ran half way up the main street but then, as Barbara drew close to the crowd the noise faltered and stopped. Head held high and her ginger hair shining in the sun, Barbara strode up to the girl and took one of her suitcases. Then she took the girl's arm and the two began to walk down the hill together.

At once there was a great cry of anger from one of the women and the whole crowd began screaming abuse and banging on their pans again. It was then that Roger, who had dodged into a shop doorway to watch, noticed that they were all women. There weren't any men there. Why weren't there any men? What was going on?

He hadn't the faintest idea but when he looked at Barbara, tall and defiant, and at the women beside her, he knew that he was with them. He rushed out of the shop doorway to the other side of the young woman, took her other case from her and took hold of her hand.

Again the noise was hushed for a little while. People were astonished to see this ten year old boy joining the two women.

178

His presence had an inhibiting effect on the screaming women and though the noise started again, it was more muted.

As the trio walked together, Barbara's chin seemed to rise higher and higher with a strange determination. They came to the boat and the fisherman helped the two women into the stern. Roger handed down the suitcases and then took his place quietly in the bows. The fisherman pushed off and then he and Roger pulled out into the centre of the current.

The crowd had been standing around menacing in their hostility but now that the boat was pulling away they began shouting again in a final crescendo of hate. The fat woman hurled the effigy into the water after the boat screaming, "Drown damme. Drown." But with the tide in their favour they were making good progress upstream back towards Beddingford. The noise from the shore faded until the peace of the river began to calm them down.

As the two women clung to one another in the stern of the boat there was nothing to be heard but the sound of the oars in the rowlocks, the drip of the water from the oars and the run of the water creaming past the bows.

When they reached Beddingford the fisherman helped the two women onto the quayside and put their cases ashore. Barbara asked how much she owed but he wouldn't hear of it.

"I never did hold with they skimmingtons," he said. "You were a danged vooull to interfere." He paused and then he added, "I've never seed nuthin finer in me life."

Then he turned to the other young woman. She had still not spoken a word. She just held on to Barbara. The fisherman spoke kindly to her, "Best of luck to ee maid. This id'n' the end of the world you know. With friends like this yer you'll be all right."

"Thank you," she whispered. "Thank you for all you have done."

She looked dazed. Roger stood nearby, uncertain what he ought to do next.

"Give me a hand with one of these cases Roger, will you?"

By the time they got to Barbara's house Roger felt as if his arms would drop off.

"I'm not going to ask you in now Roger. I hope you understand."

Yes. He understood. He would have liked to stay with them but he realised that they needed to be alone together.

"Thank you for all your help. I don't know what we'd have done without you. Come and see me again soon – tomorrow if you like."

She took him in her arms and kissed him. The other lady added her thanks and a rather red-faced Roger set off for home feeling very happy and proud. But by the time he had arrived back home he had decided not to tell Miss Holly where he had been or what he had been doing. Yet he couldn't resist asking:

"What's a skimmington?"

"What a boy it is for questions," she answered. She had gone very red and looked extremely uncomfortable. "What on earth has put it into your head to ask such a thing?"

"Oh a couple of the fishermen were talking. They said there had been a skimmington and I wondered what it was."

Miss Holly was still looking very embarrassed. "You don't want to bother your head about things like that. They id'n' for the likes of decent people like you nor me."

Roger didn't press it, but the next day he asked Barbara. Barbara said, "I thought you would want to know and I've been racking my brains to know how to tell you but I'm not very clever and it's a bit awkward. You see, Gertie is a friend of mine."

"Is that the lady who came with us?"

"Gertie. Yes. Didn't you know her name?"

"So what was yesterday all about?"

"Oh dear. How can I put it? Gertie did something that made the other women of Opstow very angry. So they decided to have a skimmington to tell her how much they hated her.

"Sometimes people just parade round the village with a dummy like a Guy Fawkes only everyone knows that the dummy is supposed to be like the woman they hate. It is a way of telling everyone in the village that the woman has done something wrong. It shames her and makes her life a misery.

"But sometimes people go further and drive a woman out of her home and out of their village. It was a bit like that with Gertie, except that she had decided to leave the village of her own free will. But when the other women heard she was going, they ganged up against her to make it look as if they were driving her out."

Roger felt that he had never heard anything so horrible in his life.

"I wish the Germans would come and bomb every one of them," he said.

"No you don't," said Barbara. "You don't wish any such thing. You just wish people would be nice to each other."

"But how could they hate Gertie so much? She seemed very nice to me."

"She is very nice and she's a good friend of mine. And I don't know how to explain things. It's a bit difficult."

Neither of them had heard Gertie come in, nor had they seen her standing in the doorway so she startled them when she spoke.

"The boy has a right to know what I did and what sort of a woman he helped."

"He's still only a boy," said Barbara.

"Yes, but he took a big risk helping us yesterday and it might have been much worse but for him." Then she turned to Roger and said, "What's your name?"

"Roger."

"Well Roger. You might not understand all I'm going to tell you, but you will remember and one day you'll understand.

"You know Barbara's married to Tom and they both love each other."

"Yes," said Roger.

"Well, love's a funny thing. Some people fall in love and stay in love and nothing changes that. But other people fall in love and fall out of love again. Well . . . I fell in love with a man who was already married but who had fallen out of love with his wife. Then I started with a baby and he told his wife he was going to leave her. She told her friends and they all got together to show me how much they hated me for taking her husband away."

"What will you do now?" asked Roger.

"My man's in the Navy but he found me a little house in Beddingford and I shall live there until my baby comes. And when he's got a bit of leave he'll come and we shall live as if we were husband and wife and one day he'll get divorced from his wife and marry me."

Roger didn't know what to say.

"I've never heard of a skimmington before," he said, "and I hope I never hear of one again. I think it's terrible what they did to you."

181

"Well it's over now," said Barbara, "so let's forget all about it." She giggled, "Now we know what it was like to be the three musketeers."

# 32

# The Runaway

It was in those early months of 1942 that Roger began to notice changes at his school. The school was shrinking. The blitz seemed to have passed its peak and many parents had decided to have their children back home again. Evacuees began to disappear back to their homes. One of those who went was Jimmy Smith. Although the bombing continued, most of them were never evacuated again.

It was after Easter that the shrinkage in the school became really noticeable. It was not only that evacuees were going home. At the top end of the school boys like Gerry had finished their schooling and left. They were not replaced by new pupils joining at the bottom end of school. And it wasn't only the children who were going. A few of the teachers had gone, some to teach back at home and others to join the armed forces.

Spring turned to summer. Late in the summer term the headmaster said that he had a special announcement to make at assembly.

"At the end of term our school will be returning home."

Everybody cheered and he let them get it out of their system before he called for quiet again. Then he added, "We have informed all your parents. We have also told them that if they prefer to keep any of you in Beddingford, you will be transferred to Beddingford grammar school. A few parents have already made it clear that that is what they wish. If you are one of those children your form teacher will tell you today. Before the end of term you will be introduced to the Beddingford headmaster and your Beddingford form master."

After assembly there was a lot of talk on the way to their class-rooms. They all wanted to go home and none of them wanted to join Beddingford. The two schools had been rivals in everything, rugby, cricket, athletics, cross country. And of course Roger thought about the old quarry gang and the Beddingford lot they fought with. "I'm not going to that school!" he thought but he didn't really expect that he would be staying. Now that everyone was going home, he would be going too.

At the end of school Mr Benfleet asked about ten of them to remain behind. Roger was one of them. Mr Benfleet told them, "We have heard from each of your parents. They all wish you to stay in the safety of Beddingford. As the headmaster told you, we have been able to make arrangements for you to continue your schooling at Beddingford grammar, so you won't have to change school buildings. And you will be happy to know that all of you will be staying in the same homes you live in now. That's all at the moment. I'll talk to you again nearer to the end of term."

None of them was happy. Roger was angry and horrified. He had been so excited at the thought of going home. Now he was told he had got to stay. He wrote to his parents pleading with them to be allowed to go home. They wrote explaining why it was better and safer for him to stay.

Night after night he lay awake thinking about it all. Many a night he cried himself to sleep. Sometimes he was miserable. Sometimes he was angry. And at once his work at school suffered. At the end of that summer term he was bottom of his class.

Miss Holly tried to comfort him. "Don't ee worry my dear," she said. "Mr Churchill was never very good at schooyull."

The summer holidays came and Roger spent a great deal of time on his own. His friends had all gone. Nearly every day he went to the sea, sometimes walking, sometimes on the bus. He spent his time swimming catching prawns, wandering over the rocks and exploring the rock pools or tramping over the cliff paths.

The old broken-down coastguard station became his second home. But for the fact that Beddingford grammar was looming he would have been perfectly happy. But in his mind he turned that school more and more into a kind of prison full of hateful people. He would not go there. He wouldn't. He wouldn't. He wouldn't.

On wet days he read endlessly. Biggles, Zane Grey cowboy books, the Saint. But there were two books he read over and over again: *Stalky and Co.* and *Tom Brown's Schooldays*. Why couldn't he go to a school like one of those instead of rotten old Beddingford grammar.

He made up his mind that whatever happened, he would not go to that school. But how could he avoid it?

He would run away.

He began to save his pocket money and to plot and plan. He checked on buses and trains. How far could he get with the money he had saved? Not very far. One penny pocket money every week didn't mount up very quickly especially as he nearly always spent a farthing or a halfpenny.

Then he hit on the idea of running away with gypsies. He wouldn't need any money for that and he could live in one of their caravans.

He was quite sure that they would be glad to have him and he began to keep his eyes open for them. But the days and weeks were slipping by and he never seemed to see any.

He was beginning to get desperate. At last he decided to live in his coastguard hut. He began to take jars and tins of food there. He took some of them from Miss Holly's pantry and some he bought with his own money. He saved up sweets and chocolate and hoarded it all in biscuit tins.

September came and the first day of the new term. During the night he had crept downstairs and taken a hunk of bread and some cakes.

He put them in his satchel with a couple of extra tins and covered them all up with his books. In the morning after breakfast he kissed Miss Holly goodbye which surprised her because he had never kissed her before. She felt rather pleased. Then he put on his mac and set out for school.

He climbed the hill and walked through the outskirts of the town towards the school. Then suddenly, he turned right instead of going straight on to school. He slipped behind a row of houses, took off his school cap and stuffed it in his pocket, and ran down to the footpath that led to the sea.

It was a beautiful day, warm and sunny, and Roger felt excited. He didn't hurry. No one would be looking for him yet. He followed the footpath along the edge of a few fields. Their high hedges were full of flowers and birds and butterflies. Then he passed into a lane between two hedges. That went on for about a mile and when he climbed the gate at the end of the lane he was within sight of the sea.

He ran across the next few fields and then the footpath took him into the bracken that marked the beginning of the cliff moorlands. He hadn't seen a single person and that made him feel safe. The bracken smelt marvellous. This was where he belonged, in the bracken by the sea. Over to the right he could see the small seaside village. He turned left and made for his coastguard hut.

It was overgrown and well hidden and rather dark and cool inside even on a hot day. Roger changed into his holiday clothes and put his school clothes away. He was already feeling hungry so he ate some of his bread. Then he went down to the rocks with his prawning net and spent a successful hour catching his main meal. He took the prawns back up to his hideaway in a bucket of sea-water. It didn't take him long to get a fire going and on it he boiled his prawns. He ate some more of his bread and butter with them and then he lay down in the bracken with the sun shining warm and strong overhead.

A pair of buzzards circled lazily high in the sky and he watched them with pleasure. He had often watched them and knew their nest well. Earlier in the year he had climbed to the top of the tree it was in and seen their two dirty white eggs marked with brown blobs.

Now he just lay in the sun until it began to cool. Then he began to cut himself armfuls of bracken. He cut it in different places so that it wouldn't be noticed and took it into his hut where he made himself a nice, thick mattress with it. Soon he had a bed of bracken to lie on that would be both soft and warm.

By now he was hungry again. He walked back inland to the fields he had passed through in the morning. There were turnips in one of them. He pulled a couple of them and then walked on to a potato field. He walked into the field away from the hedge and dug himself some potatoes.

"If I do that every day I shall be able to store enough to keep me going after the farmer digs them up," he said to himself.

Then he put his bucket and spade into the hedge and walked to the barn where the farmer kept his hens. He opened the barn door and crept inside without disturbing the farm dogs. Then he moved

186

through the barn feeling under the hens for their eggs. They stirred and grumbled a bit but not too loudly and he soon had two pockets full of eggs.

He slipped away as silently as he had come, collected his bucket of vegetables and his spade and returned to his hide-out. He built up the fire again, opened a precious tin of baked beans, heated it and made some toast. After he had eaten he changed into his pyjamas, made up his bed from all the bits of blanket and rags he had collected, covered it all with his mac and crawled in. He was nice and snug and he fell asleep right away.

The next morning he was up very early. It was another lovely day. He made his way down to the edge of the seaside village and collected a couple of bottles of milk from people's doorsteps. He hurried back onto his cliff footpaths with the milk and reckoned he was well set up now for a couple of days.

Old Sam had taught him well. He'd have been really proud of the lad. That lunch-time he got himself a proper meal. He baked himself some potatoes in the fire, warmed the rest of the baked beans, cooked a couple of eggs and ate the lot together with some raw turnip.

The day passed quickly and when darkness fell he snuggled contentedly back on his mattress. He slept soundly again.

But during the night the weather changed.

# 33

# Barbara to the Rescue

Meanwhile back in Beddingford there was consternation. Miss Holly had found a note from Roger saying that he had run away. She went straight to the police station.

The police checked at the school and found that Roger had not been to school that day. They phoned Roger's father and he promised to come immediately from London. They also phoned all the local police stations and soon the police all over the county were on the watch for Roger.

In Beddingford itself the police began calling on every house that Roger had ever lived in. Mrs Hilton gave a very black picture of 'that nasty troublesome boy' but fortunately most people gave a very different picture of him. Boys at Beddingford school suggested to the police that they search the old quarry. They told them that he used to belong to a gang that had its headquarters there.

But no one led them any nearer to Roger.

When the police called on Barbara, she was just getting herself and the baby ready to go to the station with Tom. He had been home on leave. She didn't say anything to the police but after they had gone she said to Tom, "He'll be somewhere by the sea."

"Why didn't you say?" asked Tom.

"Poor kid. Can you imagine what he'd feel like if he was picked up by the police? He'd be scared stiff."

"So what are you going to do?"

"I'm going to look for him myself, first thing in the morning. When I've got him safely home I'll tell his mum and dad. They can tell the police."

"You be careful. You don't want to get yourself into trouble," Tom said anxiously.

"Trouble? Just think of the trouble that poor kid's in."

"You're too soft with that boy."

"If they'd left him with me this would never have happened. He was happy with me."

"Yes, I suppose so. Anyone would be happy with you. I certainly am."

All this time they had been walking to the station and now it was time to part. So Tom continued, "Take care of yourself until I come 'ome again won't ee."

"Course I will – and you take care of yourself and come home safe and sound."

Thinking and talking about Roger had taken their minds off their own parting and made it easier. They kissed one another. Tom got on the train and Barbara waved it out of sight. Then she went home thinking partly about Tom and partly about Roger.

She felt lonely when she got home. She took the baby out of the push chair and put her in her cot. She was fast asleep. Then she went to bed herself and cried herself to sleep.

In the morning she was up early. She looked out of the window in dismay. The weather had changed completely. Gone was the lovely warm September sunshine. In its place there were strong winds and driving rain.

She bathed her baby and gave her her breakfast before taking her to Gertie's house and leaving her there.

Then she got herself ready. She dressed up in old clothes with raincoat and boots. She filled a flask with hot soup and set off to catch the bus. A middle-aged couple stood in front of her with two suitcases. They had just come back from their holidays. The bus came and she settled down in the seat behind the couple. She knew that Roger would be somewhere by the sea – but where? Perhaps he had a key to the beach hut he had always gone to, or perhaps he was living in a cave at the foot of the cliffs. Anyway she would find him. She was sure of that.

She looked out of the window and began half-listening to the conversation of the couple in front. But soon she was listening very carefully. The wife said to her husband, "Did they 'ave anythin' special vor ee at the station when ee called in to tell 'm you was back?"

189

"Nothin' as would interest you," he answered.

There was a moment or two's silence and then he said, "Yes there was too. Do you remember they two boys that came to us to tell us they'd seed a German submarine?"

"What about them?"

"Well one of them — the bigger one called Roger — ee's rinned away an' they can't find un."

"What de mean ee rinned away?"

"Just what I said. Most of the 'vacuees 'as gone back to Lunnon but ee stayed yer. An' ee didn' want to go to Beddingford schooyull. So ee rinned away."

"Well you know where ee'll be then don' ee," said his wife.

" 'Ow should I know?" he answered.

"Gyaw," she said. "What sort of a policeman be ee? Ee'll be in thick old coastguard station up on the hills."

"Mother you'm a wonder. That's just where ee'll be. When us gets 'ome I'll have a cup of tea and put me uniform on and go an' fetch un."

"And I shall come with ee. Us can't have you frightenin' the boy can us. Poor dear in all this rain and wind too."

Barbara couldn't believe her luck. She didn't know the coast-guard station but she did know where the hills were. She got off the bus and hurried along the sea front past all the beach huts. The wind and the rain lashed in from the sea and the sea itself was wild with great rolling waves crashing towards the shore.

She reached the foot of the hills and began to climb, and at times the bracken and the brambles broke the force of the wind and gave her a bit of shelter but she was wet through and cold.

Nor was she used to this kind of walking. It was a bit different from pushing a push-chair round the shops. But she pressed on, her eyes raking the bracken for a glimpse of the coast-guard station. She must get there first.

One mile stretched into two and there had been all sorts of side paths tempting her to take wrong directions. Some of these were narrow and overgrown and she was torn by brambles and scratched. But still she pressed on. Two miles stretched into three. How much further did these hills go?

And then she saw it. A small, square grey building over to the right, close to the edge of the cliffs. There must be a path down to it. There was. She turned and hurried to the back of the building.

190

There was no door in the opening so she saw Roger at once. He was standing looking out to sea, with his back towards her. The poor kid must be frozen stiff.

"Roger," she said.

He turned, saw who it was, and ran into her arms. As she clasped him to her she felt his small body begin to heave as he burst into tears of relief. He had been feeling so cold and miserable and lonely. Now Barbara was there he knew everything would be all right somehow.

As his tears began to dry up she pulled herself away from him.

"Just look at you," she said. "You're all wet from my mac. I've got some soup somewhere. We'll have some and then pack your things and you can come home with me."

His face tightened and became obstinate.

"I can't," he said.

"What do you mean, you can't?" she asked as she pulled her flask from her bag.

"I can't go home with you because I'm not going to go to Beddingford school. And if I go home with you they'll make me."

She gave him some soup and took some herself.

"The police are looking for you and they know where you are. In fact they'll be here very soon so we shall be caught if we don't hurry. And everybody is worried about you – your mum and dad and . . . oh everybody."

"Well if the police are coming I shall have to find somewhere else – and I must get away quick. You can tell everybody that I'm OK."

"Come home with me tonight. You can have a nice bath and snuggle up with me in bed where it's warm. Then tomorrow you can talk to your mum and dad. If they still want you to go to Beddingford school you can always run away again. But at least come home tonight."

All the time she was talking she was busy picking up his things. He began to help her. He took the tins of food he had taken from Miss Holly.

"If I came home with you I could give these back to Miss Holly couldn't I?"

"Of course you could. Who's Miss Holly?" asked Barbara busily packing all the time.

"She's the lady I live with now. She's a nice old lady and ever so

191

kind. I'd like to give her her tins back. And there's something else."

"What's that?"

"Promise you won't tell."

"I won't tell. What is it?"

"You won't tell *anybody*, not until after the war?"

Barbara had a job to keep a straight face but she managed it.

"I won't say a word to anybody, not until you tell me I can."

"Not even Tom or your friend Gertie?

"Not even Tom or Gertie."

He cleared away stones and old dead bracken from a corner of the coastguard station and carefully drew out his mother's china. Barbara was astonished. She packed it with the rest of his things, wrapping clothing around it all. She was just going to ask about it when they heard voices.

"Quick," said Roger. "Let's get out and hide."

They grabbed their bags, rushed out of the door and round the coastguard station. Roger led the way along a narrow cliff path. He knew every inch of these hills. Barbara followed and they made their escape. Then they turned and began to walk inland.

No sooner had they got away than Albert and Betsy arrived.

"There's certainly been someone here," Albert said.

"But he isn't here now," answered Betsy, "and if you asks me he hasn't been gone long."

"Why do you say that?"

"Well everything's tidy and untidy if you zee what I mane."

"No I can't say as I do."

"Look around ee. The main look of the place is tidy. The bed is tidy. There's wood for a fire. That's tidy. There's some tateys and a couple of turmuts an' they'm all tidy. Ee's a proper tidy boy. But there id'n' no clothes an' there id'n' no other food an' there's a few things untidy like, as if they've been knocked or thrown aside while ee was hurryin' to get away."

"What de think Mother? De think ee see'd us comin?"

"Yes I reckon. An' ee's too smart to come back yer. Poor boy. Let's hope someone catches up with un quick. Us had better get back and you can telephone to Beddingford."

So they set off for home. By that time Barbara and Roger were well on the way to Barbara's home. The weather was so bad that there weren't many people about as they walked through Beddingford so they got home without any more trouble.

As they came near to Barbara's home she called at Gertie's house to collect her baby. Roger stood back out of sight.

"Where on earth have you been? You look half drowned," Gertie said.

"Never mind where I've been – and I can't stop. Can you come and baby-sit for me about half past nine tonight?"

"Half past nine."

"Yes. It's important – and quite exciting really. I'll tell you all about it when you come. But make sure you don't come early."

"All right then. But can't you tell me now."

"No I can't. I must get home and into a bath as quick as I can," and with that Barbara left.

Gertie watched her go and then saw a filthy little urchin she recognised run past her house to catch up with Barbara. It was that boy from the skimmington. He must be something to do with it. What was it all about?

Barbara and Roger hurried home. Once indoors Barbara almost ran Roger upstairs and into the bathroom.

"You have a good hot bath. Stay in the water until you feel warm right through. But don't be too long because I want a bath after you I'm freezing. I'll put Tom's pyjamas outside the door and his dressing gown. They'll keep you nice and warm.

So as the geyser roared and rumbled away Roger stripped off and got into the bath. He put his clothes outside the door and Barbara took those for washing. While she was waiting she saw to her baby. But Roger didn't take long. He came down looking fresh and clean and almost smothered in Tom's clothes. They had a good laugh at that and Barbara poured Roger a cup of tea.

"Now you look after the baby while I get bathed and warm," she said. "I'm perishing."

She ran upstairs and had her bath, came down in her nightdress and dressing gown and got them both a good hot meal. While they ate she asked him, "Where does that Miss Holly live?"

He told her the address.

"And what are we going to do with your china? Are you going to tell me about that?"

"It's my mum's."

"Oh well we shall be able to give it back to her when we see her won't we."

"*No!*" You don't understand. My dad mustn't see it."

193

j

"Oh. That's why I've got to keep it secret is it."

"Yes, well and there's other things too."

"What a lot of mysteries. Are you going to tell me? It sounds exciting."

So he began to tell her, slowly at first and then it all poured out and all about his trouble at the Hiltons. She was fascinated. When he had finished she cuddled him and said, "I expect a lot of people might think you've been a bit naughty but I think you've been very brave and nice to your mum too. Let's wash it and pack it and put it all away in a nice box where it will be safe."

So they put it in her bedroom and then went to bed together. He snuggled into her soft, warm body happily and was asleep within moments. She waited a little while and then slipped quietly out of bed. She got dressed and went downstairs to watch for Gertie's arrival. She came on the dot of half past nine.

"I can't stop," said Barbara. "I'll tell you everything when I get back."

"It's that little boy isn't it, that Roger?"

"That's right. They're both asleep up there. Baby's in her room and Roger's in my bed. I'll be as quick as I can."

Then she went out again into the pouring rain. She walked to Miss Holly's house and knocked her up. Miss Holly was already in bed but she couldn't sleep for worrying. She was so relieved and happy to hear that Roger was safe. She had a good cry and then pulled herself together.

"I must go and tell that poor boy's parents. They've come up from Lunnon way. An' I'd better tell the police too."

"You'll need my address. Get the police to lay off until we go to see them. Then you can bring Roger's parents to my house tomorrow and we can start putting things right. I hope people won't be hard on him. He's a lovely boy."

"He *is* a lovely boy dear. You're quite right. So you and me together must make sure everything is all right for him. Now, if you'll excuse me I'll go and get dressed and do my errands."

"And I'll get back to my baby-sitter. See you tomorrow."

She hurried home and she and Gertie had a long natter in which she told Gertie the whole story, including the secret tale of the china. After all, that was too good to miss out. It was well past midnight before Gertie made her way home and Barbara went back to bed.

194

## 34

# The Women Take Charge

The following morning Mr and Mrs Wallace called a taxi. They picked up Miss Holly and then drove to Barbara's house. Barbara welcomed them at the door and showed them into her front room.

Roger was already in there looking very pale and tense. Miss Holly pushed her way in before Mr and Mrs Wallace.

"Hello dear. 'Ow be ee? 'Tis lovely to see ee lookin' zo well. Us've been proper worried about ee."

Her prattle began to ease the tension and then Roger's mother opened her arms to her boy. She knew George would not approve. He felt that they must all be stern and strong. But she was the boy's mother after all.

He flew to her and she held him close. Mr Wallace was the only one who didn't have tears in his eyes.

Then Barbara offered them all tea and Miss Holly went out to help her.

"You've been very kind dearie."

"No I haven't," answered Barbara. "That boy's had a raw deal. I was always fond of him. I feel as if I love him like my own son."

"Yes dear. I feel just the same. But why did he run away? Is it really all about that schooyull?"

"Yes, that's it. He doesn't want to go to that school. If they try to make him, he'll run away again. I'm sure of it."

They carried the tea and biscuits in to the front room where Roger was telling them why he had run away and how Barbara had found him.

When he had finished Mr Wallace turned to Barbara and said,

"We're very grateful to you Mrs er, Mrs er . . . "

"Barbara," she said. "Call me Barbara. Everyone does."

"Well, er, Barbara, we are very grateful to you. But now I must take Roger down to the police station. They will want to have a word with him about all the trouble he has caused. And then I must take him up to the school to apologise to the headmaster and to arrange for him to begin his schooling."

Roger had gone very pale when his father talked about going to the police station. But when he went on to talk about the school Roger began to look obstinate and stubborn. His eyes grew hard and his little chin set firm. Barbara saw it and knew that there was going to be trouble if she couldn't stop it.

"Excuse me Mr Wallace, but couldn't I take Roger to the police station? They will want to see me as well – especially as I didn't let on to their policeman at Hoe village." She laughed. "I expect I shall be in just as much trouble as Roger."

"I think that's a good idea." It was Miss Holly this time. "I expects you knows the police at the station and that'll make it easier for everyone. Besides, you don't want to go seeing the police Mr Wallace. 'Tis better to keep out of their way, I always say."

Mrs Wallace had been watching very carefully. She had seen her son's face while her husband was talking and she felt that Barbara and Miss Holly were trying to protect her boy. She respected them both. They had both looked after Roger and they were both fond of him. She needed to talk to them before her husband had a chance to put his foot in it, so before he could say a word she said:

"That sounds very sensible to me. The police will want to see Barbara, so she might as well take Roger with her. And it'll give us a chance to have a good chat with Miss Holly."

Mr Wallace was not very pleased. He was the boy's father after all. He was the one who should take responsibility – but before he could say a word Miss Holly was talking.

"Roger dear you do as your mother says. You go and get ready and Barbara will take you down to the police station to have a chat with the sergeant – he's such a nice man that sergeant." (She hadn't a clue whether it really would be a sergeant they saw or what he would be like, but there was no use frightening the boy, and she felt that Barbara was quite capable of handling the whole

196

police force if necessary.)

"Now run along dear. Your mum and dad will come home with me and we'll get a nice bit of dinner – and Barbara will come home with you dear, and she'll have a bit of dinner with us I'm sure. You will won't you."

"Yes, I'd love to," answered Barbara as she began to collect up the cups and saucers.

Mrs Wallace collected those that Barbara couldn't carry and followed her into the kitchen.

"You're trying to protect my son from something Barbara," she said. "What is it?"

"We're playing for time, Miss Holly and me. We don't want you and Mr Wallace to make a mistake. It's so hard for you living up in London and all that. Roger's a good boy Mrs Wallace. Don't you let anybody tell you any different. If my baby grows up to be like him I shall be very proud."

"But what are we to do? We daren't take him home. The bombs are terrible – and we've two boys in the RAF and I expect Gerry will have to go. We could lose them all."

"I don't know what's to be done Mrs Wallace but Roger really does feel strongly about Beddingford school. He says he won't go and if he's made to go he says he'll run away again. I think he would too."

"He always did say he wouldn't go to that school. I'm afraid I never took him seriously. It looks as if we shall have to though. Thank you for telling me, and thank you for all you have done for him."

Back in the front room they all got ready to leave. While Mr and Mrs Wallace were talking to Barbara, Miss Holly took the chance to whisper to Roger, "Don' ee worry about thick school my dear. I think us can find a way out for ee. Just you leave it to your mother and me."

"What do you mean?" asked Roger.

She put her finger to her lips. "That's my secret," she said, "but don't ee worry. Everything will be all right. You'll see."

She left with his parents and Roger and Barbara set out with the baby. She left her baby with Gertie again so that it was just the two of them who presented themselves to the desk sergeant at the police station.

Before long they found themselves in an interview room with

a young officer sitting behind a table and a police constable standing by the door. Barbara moved her chair well back from the table so that the police officer could get a good view of her. Roger sat beside her.

The young officer was very much on his dignity and began to lecture Roger in a fairly heavy handed way, but Barbara interrupted him.

"Excuse me officer."

She straightened her skirt and her knees peeped out. They were rather nice knees the officer thought. He was irritated with himself for being distracted.

"Yes, what is it?"

"I think I ought to apologise."

"Apologise?"

Now Barbara was the sort of person who could usually say exactly what she meant very simply and very clearly. Yet what followed was so garbled that even Roger had difficulty in understanding what it was all about.

Barbara talked about going to search for Roger and being on the bus and overhearing a conversation and realising it was about Roger and that police officer and his wife were so clever to know exactly where Roger would be. She really did think the police were wonderful and anyway she – she paused while she crossed her legs and straightened her skirt again she really did have a very attractive, slim pair of legs – she knew that she must get there first and she found the boy and she knew that she really ought to have taken him to Hoe police station but what with the weather and them being so cold and soaked, and she didn't want him to catch his death of, and she was a bit worried about herself too what with having a small baby, and as a result they had had to wait for Miss Holly, but that wasn't too long to wait was it?

Her free leg was swinging gently. Her slim ankle and foot seemed to move almost in an arc to and fro, to and fro. The constable by the door looked almost hypnotised. The officer ran his finger round the inside of his collar. It was dreadfully hot in this interview room. His face was burning.

Even Roger found that he was looking at Barbara as he had never looked at her before. He had always thought that she was beautiful with that wonderful mane of ginger hair. And where his mother was short and dumpy, nice and comfortable looking,

Barbara was slim and nicely shaped. He supposed he had seen her legs before, but not to take notice. Alfie and Eric seemed to like noticing ladies' legs. Looking at Barbara now, Roger felt that he was beginning to understand.

Her story had left the police officer completely bemused. He hadn't followed her rigmarole at all except that she seemed to be singing the praises of old Albert down at Hoe village. It was a change to have a bit of praise from the public. Perhaps he didn't need to be too harsh. He cleared his throat.

She hitched her skirt a fraction higher and looked at him wide-eyed, ready to hang upon his every word. It was hopelessly disconcerting. He cleared his throat again.

"I wonder if you would mind just writing out what you have told us about how much help you received from the police and from Constable Robinson and his wife in particular. And . . ." – She really was a fascinating woman. Pity she was married. – "And perhaps you would make it clear to the boy what a lot of trouble he has caused."

He looked at the boy. What was it Constable Robinson had said about him? Spotted a Gerry U boat or something once. No – it wasn't necessary to lay things on too thick. Looked a respectable enough lad. What was the woman saying?

"Of course officer. Whatever you say. And we're so sorry for all the trouble you've had."

"That's nothing to the trouble I'm going to have," he thought. "I shall dream about this bloody woman for weeks. 'Whatever you say officer'. Oh if only she really meant that."

He drew the interview to a close and Barbara wrote out her statement before leaving. The desk sergeant winked at her as she left.

"Well done Miss." And then he noticed the officer standing, watching her go. He coughed and added, "You did well to find the boy."

# 35

# Miss Holly Finds the Answer

That Saturday Mr and Mrs Wallace and Miss Holly had been having their own very serious conversation. Miss Holly had kept on endlessly about what a good boy Roger was, what a dear boy he was, and what a clever boy he was and it was that which brought up the subject of school.

"You know," said Mrs Wallace, "he has always said that he didn't want to go to Beddingford school. In fact he said that he *wouldn't* go. I always pooh poohed it. I said, 'of course he would go – and enjoy it too'. But that's why he ran away, just because he didn't want to go to that school."

"Well he is going to go and that's that," said Mr Wallace. "I'm going to have a good chat to him as soon as I can get him on my own and then I'll take him to see his new headmaster."

"He was bottom of the class last term," said Miss Holly, "and him such a clever boy too."

"What's that supposed to mean?" asked Mr Wallace irritably. He was beginning to wish that Miss Holly wasn't there.

"It means that as soon as ee knew that ee wasn't going home to you like all the other 'vacuees, ee got miserable and his school work suffered."

"Yes," said Mrs Wallace. "That's what the school said."

"Stuff and nonsense," grumbled Mr Wallace although he felt deep down that the school was probably right. But Miss Holly hadn't finished:

"If you make him go to Beddingford school, I think his work will go on suffering. Ee'll either keep rinning away, or he'll sulk and stay bottom of the class. An' that would be sad with him such a clever boy – yes and such a happy boy mostly."

"But what else can we do?" Mrs Wallace asked. 'We just don't feel that it is safe enough for him to come home with all the bombing that's going on. If we are not very careful we could lose all our children what with Alfie and Eric in the Air Force. We must keep Roger and Margaret safe."

"Yes and Margaret is all fixed up isn't she?" said Miss Holly. Both parents felt that what Miss Holly meant was that they had taken the trouble to fix things up for Margaret but not for Roger, but that wasn't fair.

"You mean that we have sent her to boarding school. Well, she wasn't old enough to go to Beddingford Grammar was she? Besides, with Miss Binns going back to London we felt she needed to be looked after properly."

"An' quite right too I hope," said Miss Holly doubtfully. She felt that Margaret was too young for boarding school but she didn't say so. Instead she said, "Do you know what Roger's favourite books are?"

Mr Wallace felt that this old woman was a proper muddle. What had Roger's favourite books got to do with this conversation about his schooling. So he left the conversation to his wife. "No," she said. "What are they?"

"*Stalky and Co.* and *Tom Brown's Schooldays*," answered Miss Holly triumphantly as if she was a magician taking rabbits out of a top hat.

"*Stalky and Co.* and *Tom Brown's Schooldays*," said Mrs Wallace looking baffled. "I don't quite see . . . "

"They're both books about boarding schooyulls."

"What of it?" Mr Wallace felt he had been left out of this conversation long enough.

"There's a boarding schooyull out in the middle of the country not many miles from yer. 'Tis called Perspins College."

"And you think that if we sent Roger to Perspins College all our troubles would be at an end," Mrs Wallace said with a smile.

"Out of the question," said Mr Wallace. "We could never afford it. It's bad enough having to pay Margaret's fees let alone having to pay for Roger as well." Mr Wallace paused. "What was the name of that school?"

"Perspins College," said Miss Holly, " 'an my nevvy says ee's got enough petrol to take you out to look at it if you'd like to go."

"When could he take us?" asked Mrs Wallace.

"This afternoon if I zee to the shop vor un."

"I want it to be clearly understood that there is no way we can manage it." Mr Wallace felt he was being driven into a corner and his wife made quite sure that he couldn't get out of it when she said:

"But it might be nice just to go and have a look, and I'm sure we could spare a couple of our petrol coupons for your nephew."

By the time Barbara arrived with her baby and with Roger it had been decided that they would go if Barbara could look after Roger for the rest of the day. Miss Holly put Barbara in the picture and asked her not to say anything to Roger in case Mr Wallace didn't let him go.

So, after lunch Roger, Barbara and the baby went off on their own while Miss Holly took Mr and Mrs Wallace to the shop. She took over the shop and her nephew drove them out into the country to see the school. They had barely stopped the car when a man like a whirlwind in a black gown strode across to meet them.

He was the headmaster, a dynamic, no nonsense disciplinarian who made an immediate impression on Mr Wallace. With barely a glance at the school (which looked like a fairly ramshackle set of farm buildings) they were whisked into the headmaster's study. Half an hour later they were drinking tea with the headmaster's elegant wife. Swept along by the headmaster's enthusiasm they had signed Roger up for the school and agreed that he would start the following Monday.

As they drove back to Beddingford they felt slightly bemused and hoped with all their heart that they had done the right thing.

Barbara brought Roger back to Miss Holly's that evening. They all had a cup of tea but there was an awkwardness in the conversation because they all knew that the subject of school had got to be faced. When Mr Wallace stood up and tapped out his pipe by the fire his wife realised that they were in for one of his speeches. That was the last thing they wanted, so she broke the ice herself.

"Your father and I have been talking about your schooling. You know that Margaret will be going to boarding school? Well Miss Holly knows of a boarding school for boys which is in the country not far from here."

"A boarding school?" Roger's eyes lit up.

" 'Tis a bit like *Stalky and Co.* and *Tom Brown's Schooldays*," whispered Miss Holly though she never dreamed that it could almost have been modelled on those two establishments.

"*Stalky and Co.* and *Tom Brown's Schooldays*," breathed Roger excitedly.

Mr Wallace was not too happy at the way in which he had been pre-empted. Now it was his turn.

"The school is called Perspins College. Your mother and I went to the school this afternoon and arranged with the headmaster for you to begin your schooling there on Monday. Now I don't want any more nonsense about this. You either go to this school or to Beddingford and there's . . . "

He got no further. To his astonishment his son rushed to him and clung to him. He rather enjoyed the sensation.

"Boarding school. Oh Dad." And then he rushed to his mother. His eyes shone. "Oh Mother," and he hugged her. "Just like *Stalky and Co.* and *Tom Brown's Schooldays*." He hugged Miss Holly. "I'm not going to rotten old Beddingford." He almost shouted it and then he ran and hugged Barbara.

It was as if a cloud had been lifted from the room. The relief was intense. He was so happy.

With just a hint of anxiety Mrs Wallace and Miss Holly wondered if the boy would be as happy at Perspins as he expected to be. Only time would tell. They hoped they had done the right thing. He was certainly happy now. Happiness is such an intangible thing. They felt that they must make the most of it while it lasted. As they looked at him their anxieties were silenced, at least for the time. His happiness infected them all.

All the decisions had been taken. Everything properly sorted out. Now George couldn't wait to get back home and back to work. But for once Lilian decided to stick her neck out. With Miss Holly and Barbara in the room she felt that George would be unlikely to argue no matter what he felt.

"When do you plan to go home George?"

"I thought we'd take the mid-morning train tomorrow now everything's settled."

"If you don't mind George, you go tomorrow and I'll stay and see Roger into school. And I can go and see how Margaret is settling in as well."

He flushed. She hadn't discussed this with him. He wasn't at all sure that he liked the thought of her dealing with head-teachers on her own. She had always needed a man to look after her. He noticed Miss Holly and the other woman looking at him. He felt it was a bit awkward. He didn't want to look mean or – oh why not. If that was what Lilian wanted.

"Of course my dear. That sounds an excellent idea."

They almost felt the tension dissolve and the atmosphere relax. And it was then that Barbara had an idea. She invited Mrs Wallace and Miss Holly to come to her house for tea on Sunday and to bring Roger too. And she gave Miss Holly just enough of a hint for that lady to say at once:

"What a lovely idea. Us would love to come wouldn't us Mrs Wallace?"

Lilian wasn't at all sure that she would but she could hardly say so, so she agreed.

She and Roger saw George off at the station the following morning. Mr Wallace had had some serious things to say to Roger about all that he expected of him at his new school and Roger was prepared to promise the moon. Again he hugged his father and again his father felt that it was a rather pleasing sensation. Perhaps his son wasn't such a bad lad after all.

They went back to Miss Holly for lunch and Miss Holly gave Lilian a note from Barbara.

"Could you possibly spare a few minutes with me in private before you come to tea. It concerns Roger and I think it is important. I shall be indoors all day today."

So after lunch Lilian said that she needed to make some arrangements to see Margaret and set off on her own. What on earth could the young woman want?

When she came to Barbara's house she was surprised to find Barbara rather awkward and uncomfortable.

"What on earth is it?"

"I'm in a very difficult position Mrs Wallace. I wouldn't be speaking to you at all if I didn't think you were a kind and understanding sort of mother."

Oh dear. This sounded like trouble. This young woman had been shielding him from something. She was talking again.

"I know that he did wrong Mrs Wallace. But he did it for you,

you see. He really did. Well and to get back at them a bit I suppose. That too, but it was mostly for you. And I promised him I wouldn't say anything, not to anybody. And if I do tell you, you mustn't let on, not when he tells you himself. Only I thought I might be able to persuade him to tell you tea time when you come. And then it would be all over with and he can start this new school with a clean plate." She stopped and giggled nervously. "I didn't mean that. Well I did, but it's quite funny really."

Mrs Wallace was as bemused as the police officer had been.

"Barbara," she said, "I haven't the faintest idea what you have been talking about. But you and Miss Holly have been so kind to Roger that I feel bound to be guided by you both. You seem to care about the boy and you both seem to believe in him. So what is all this about?"

Barbara hesitated. "Let me show you," she said.

She left the room and came back with a box. She opened the lid and took out a small package which she unwrapped carefully.

"My china," whispered Mrs Wallace. "So he did steal the china."

"But in his little mind it wasn't stealing," said Barbara. "The only things he took were your four cups, saucers and plates. Mr Wallace had told him again and again how upset you were to lose that china so he decided to get it back for you."

"My china. My precious china. My mother gave this to me for a wedding present," said Mrs Wallace. "But how did he do it? We searched everywhere?"

"He took it in the middle of the night and hid it in a cave. Then when all the fuss died down he took it to the coastguard station where he had a sort of hideaway – the place he has been in these last few days. When I fetched him he let me in on the secret, but only after I promised faithfully that I would tell no one."

"So what is your plan now?"

"I thought I would try to persuade him to give it to you at tea time. You could be all surprised and thrilled even though he had been rather a naughty boy. And then you could take it home with you."

"And somehow, one day in the future I shall have to fool George into thinking that I've found some spares in a sale somewhere. Hm. I can't tell you what it means to me to have this china back again Barbara. I can't feel cross with the boy. But you know, he looked us all straight in the face and swore that he never stole . . . " She paused. "The clever little devil. He looked at Mr Hilton and swore that he never stole *their* china and that's what he said to me too. So in his own mind it wasn't stealing and he wasn't telling lies."

Barbara laughed. "My Tom's school report once said, 'If he's not hanged first, I shall follow his career with interest.' If Roger doesn't grow up to be a crook, perhaps he'll be a lawyer."

"Let's hope it's a lawyer," said Lilian grimly, but she agreed to Barbara's plan.

On Sunday they were all there and Margaret too. Barbara took Roger to one side and pointed out that this was a wonderful chance to give his mother her present because his father wasn't there. Roger wasn't at all sure but he allowed himself to be persuaded. After tea he brought the box and gave it to his mother.

She put it on the floor beside her chair, opened the top and took out a small package. She unwrapped it carefully.

"My china," she whispered. "Oh Roger you naughty boy. You shouldn't have done this. It is the best present I've ever had."

She unwrapped each piece and placed them all on the table.

Then she took Roger in her arms and hugged him. The tears poured down her face and Barbara's and Roger's. Miss Holly dabbed her eyes quickly and turned her attention to Margaret who hadn't a clue what all this fuss was about.

When people had calmed down it was Miss Holly who said, "I think they still use enamel mugs at Perspins College. Your mum won't want any of those."

They all roared with laughter. Neither Roger nor Margaret was aware of it but evacuation was over. They might not be going home but they were starting a new chapter in their lives, a chapter that would carry them well beyond the end of the war.